To Stephanie:
Congratulations. I
hope something in this
enhances what you do
The Tribbet
Sept 30, 1994

Making

Their

Mark

Making

Their

Mark:

Educating

African-American

Children

Dr. Israel Tribble, Jr

Beckham House Publishers, Inc/ Silver Spring, MD

Published in the United States by
Beckham House Publishers, Inc.
P.O. Box 8008, Silver Spring, MD 20907
ISBN: 0-931761-33-6
ISBN: 0-931761-30-1 (paperback)

1098765432

CONTENTS

Acknowledgements

I would like to acknowledge the consultation, contributions, research and editing assistance provided by Dr. Carolyn Tucker. Her interest, commitment and the use of some of her ablest graduate students were absolutely critical to the early preparation of this manuscript.

I would also like to thank the many friends and colleagues who have tolerated and challenged me over thirty years in education in this country. The ideas articulated here did not emerge quickly or without some growing pains. They have been honed by experience and further refined by education and training.

I would also like to thank Mrs. Joycelyn Reed for her expert typing assistance and her willingness to re-type and re-type and sometimes re-type again. To her I owe a very deep debt of gratitude.

I want to acknowledge the growing relationship between the author and his editor. Barry Beckham makes writing and publishing exciting through his expert knowledge of the craft, his personal commitment to quality and his understanding of the human condition, especially as it relates to African Americans. Thanks for being you.

1

A Cow That Has No Tail Can Not Chase Flies

The secret of the twenty-first century for African Americans is how we can turn from individual accomplishment to collective achievement.

My eye in this book is on improving African-American academic achievement. I mean group or aggregate achievement--the people as a whole, rather than individual achievement, examples of which there are thousands.

Strangely enough, when we achieve, our examples are seen as successful individual circumstances rather than group experiences. Benjamin Banneker's building of the first clock in the United States is weighed as an example of one man's achieving. The same is true of Madame C.J. Walker's becoming the first Black woman millionaire or of Lewis Howard Latimer's receiving a patent for the electric lamp.

11

They are always seen as instances of extraordinary individual merit rather than as examples of how Black people have achieved as a group. Further, despite the hard evidence to the contrary, the potential for group achievement has also been overlooked.

One of the many reasons that the public school system is failing to educate our youngsters is that it neither sees nor identifies this capacity for group achievement. Therefore, the system does very little to encourage this attainment. In their minds, Banneker and Walker and Latimer and the Black student who made the honor roll are "different" from the rest. They are not seen as a part of the group experience with which we're all familiar, but instead as exceptional individual examples. Yet all of us in America, regardless of our color, have seen successful African Americans achieving. It is a scenario repeated a thousandfold every day.

In fact, barring brain damage, any child can learn and achieve. This attitude must be the basis for reversing the poor levels of both educational achievement and expectation among African Americans so that we aspire toward greater group achievement. This is the end toward which we must move. By inspiring greater numbers of African-American youth toward collective achievement, we enhance the attainment of the group itself. But the key is that we must inspire greater numbers.

I present this plan after being in education for 30 years. I started out as the first academic Black teacher in Plainfield High School in New Jersey where I earned $4850 yearly. Since then my experience has been spent on the secondary level, in higher education and in government. Now I run a 20 million-dollar quasi-public institution, the Florida Endowment Fund for Higher Education, based in Tampa.

I stumbled into achievement. I chose education as a career almost by default. There were not that many options. Either I had to be a Jackie Robinson--an outstanding athlete--or a teacher. But if I have learned anything from my experience, it is that I was fortunate enough to have an opportunity to reach my capabilities. I had a chance to make a mark.

Once I started reaching my goals, I became hell bent upon an ultimate (and still unachieved) goal--becoming a college president before age 40. Then I began to understand a lesson that is also an important part of this formula for inspiring success. You are not always in control of your destiny and must therefore be content sometimes with simply preparing yourself as well as you can for however you will make your mark.

It isn't necessary, I tell young people, to know exactly how and what you will do to make your contribution. It is only necessary to train and prepare yourself to be successful. "The cow that has no tail cannot chase flies," goes the African proverb. If you do the best you can, something will come out of it.

Are our African-American youth getting either of these messages in the public school system? I am sorry to say that they are not.

My reason for setting down these thoughts is not just to argue that, in the public school system in America, certain important philosophical premises are missing. I want to go farther than that to offer a blueprint, a plan for enhancing the group achievement of our youth. Just as Benjamin Banneker in 1792 reproduced from memory the plans for laying out the city of Washington, DC, I too want to lay out a plan based on my memory--of what I know after 30 years about the public school system's continuous abridgement of African-American academic achievement. At the heart of my plan is the belief that we must create models that focus on student empowerment rather than focusing on how to change the system or institution.

After describing my own background of lowly origins and how I was fortunate enough to be encouraged to look beyond that limited landscape, I point out how important it is to tell African-American youth that their forefathers' beginnings were neither in the cotton fields nor in the tobacco fields.

The tradition of African contributions to the world may have been suppressed and disrupted, but they cannot be ignored. We shall rise again. I want our youth to know that we shall rise again--as high in stature as the pyramids, built by their ancestors and still unduplicative. Any program for raising educational achievement must emphasize the enhancing of self esteem. Think about how much higher their self worth can be raised when they are told the truth about their background. They came from someplace else, not from the fields. And

13

therefore they can change--and become great achievers like Estevanico, Hannibal, St. Augustine, Pushkin, Mary McLeod Bethune, Gwendolyn Brooks and a host of others.

Next, in chapter three, I maintain that African-American children in this country's public education system have failed at a rate that is disproportionately high despite the host of programs designed over the last thirty years to improve their performance. These efforts have floundered because they have not attacked the root causes: the institutionalized low expectation levels and the oppressive social conditions which enfeeble African-American children on a daily basis.

At the center of these conditions is institutionalized racism which has set up two major barriers to Black achievement. First, our children are culturally isolated. The American public school system is an ethnocentric entity, maintaining and protecting the status quo of Anglo-Saxon civilization at the cost of denying non-white students pride in their own culture and a sense of connectivity.

Secondly, the double standard established by the school system in their labeling process results in African-American youth being identified as behavior problems, learning disabled and other designations that eventually cut their chances of reaching their full potential. Until we abandon the practices and premises behind the old programs and consequently change the school environments, our children will never achieve adequately.

In chapter four, I expand on the idea of cultural isolation by contending that our people have never had our cultural values or human needs represented within the walls of the public schools. Since the mission of these schools is to preserve and transmit the majority culture, they cannot be expected to be agents of change. So we have to establish settings outside of the school system, modeled somewhat on the traditional Asian-American and Jewish-American types, to foster not only an understanding of cultural heritage, but also of academic achievement.

In order to develop a new philosophy of education that prepares Black citizens for educational success in America, we must understand certain critical assumptions. I discuss the background of these assumptions in chapter five, making it clear that in order to achieve group educational success for our youth, we must change the very lifestyle that these children emulate.

In chapter six, I explain why my blueprint for this group educational excellence depends upon marshalling the considerable resources of the African-American community. It is there that our children can receive the supplemental education steeped in African-American values and traditions that is essential to a group achievement ethic. Nurtured systematically under this culture, our youngsters will be motivated to view educational achievement as a positive experience that requires learning beyond the classroom.

Next, I present five models designed to deal with the many conflicts which exist within the public school system. These conflicts relate to African-American children in particular and all children in general. Community organizations should consider these models as a set of alternative strategies to be used singularly or in combination.

Finally, in chapter eight, I lay out the basic assumptions that are essential to educational success and then describe how the McKnight Programs in Higher Education were launched in Florida.

I end by asking some key questions about where we are headed at the end of the century, but reiterate the importance of communities' developing strategies to motivate and love all of its children. They are our future, and it is up to us to make the difference for the ''dark and different.''

2

It Is the Rainy Season That Brings Wealth

"Y ou can make a mark for your race," he said.

I was sixteen, a sophomore at Vineland High School in Vineland, New Jersey, a sleepy town 30 miles east of Philadelphia. Earlier that day he had banished me from his biology class for misbehaving and sent me to the principal's office. The principal had admonished me with a combination of sober looks and severe assessments of my treating a frog with such vile disrespect, and now I was back in Mr. Krouse's room.

Marlin P. Krouse was a no-nonsense German-American who combed his hair to the side and wore spectacles. Now he was looking at me with the strait-laced seriousness that was his trademark, but what he had just said would have the greatest effect on me. In fact, it would stay with me to this very day as one of the most important statements

16

every made to me.

He had actually suggested that I could be somebody. And further-more, that he expected me to be somebody. ''You can do better than you are doing,'' he continued.

Nobody outside of my family had said anything like that to me in my life. It was such a novel concept that it stunned me. Those words helped change my life.

Some day I will make a mark.

What was he saying? He was delivering the message of hope and high expectation that every African-American youngster whose circumstances are mired in poverty needs to hear. His declaration has since become a central theme in my blueprint for educating African-American youth. In fact, it is the philosophical centerpiece of this discussion about how we can ensure that our youth are educated properly.

We must emphasize to our youth that some day, they too will make a mark, that someday, they too will reach goals and succeed beyond their wildest expectations, achieving against all odds. But the lesson must go even beyond that point of raising self esteem. There has to be an accompanying statement which says that where you start is not the same place where you end up. And barring brain damage, anybody can learn.

To explain why I am driven by this basic philosophical premise sparked by a New Jersey biology teacher--that your origins and background do not limit your potential--it is necessary to talk about where I came from. My cultural background is not at all dissimilar to that of the majority of Black youth in America. But my lowly origins and background didn't stop me. And we must tell them that their backgrounds should not stop them.

In 1940 my mother, Fannie Louise Thomas arrived in Camden, New Jersey by bus from Cape Charles, Virginia to visit her aunt. My mother was seventeen. She had left school after the fifth grade to help support her seven brothers and sisters. She had neither academic nor vocational skills. No one in her family had ever finished high school, owned property or had even received an honorable discharge from the military.

Fannie Louise Thomas was introduced to Israel Tribble by her sister. He was 32 years old and married. He dated her that very first day and abused her sexually. So he, Israel Tribble became my father-- a man with a limited educational background and few marketable skills.

He was never a family provider. He used alcohol heavily and this practice no doubt made his disposition even more nasty. I only saw him two or three times in my life, meeting him for the first time when I was 19. Needless to say, I've never thought of myself as having a real father.

Now pregnant, my mother was put out of her house by Aunt Fannie. Fortunately, Aunt Irene, my father's sister, invited her to stay in her house.

One cold, blustery winter morning during my mother's first trimester, she was working as a window washer. She was wiping a glass pane with nearly frozen fingers when a Black woman walking down the street stopped and observed her.

"You should not be outside in your condition," she said. "Come home with me. I have a room you can stay in. Can you do domestic work?"

My mother answered affirmatively to this windfall of opportunity. Now she had both a home and employment possibilities--for this woman as well as others in the area.

When it was time for Mother to give birth, she struggled out of the house by herself, lumbered to a corner and hailed a cab to Philadelphia's Hahnemann Hospital.

"I heard all of the other women crying out in the delivery room next to mine," she told me, "so I bit my tongue to keep from screaming. I delivered you all alone and in silence."

As she prepared to leave the hospital with me, her newborn son, the doctor asked her if she had a place to go and someone to look after her. She replied, "Of course" and went back to her room in the Black woman's home. But even that arrangement became stressful as one of the older male roomers in the house insisted on coming into her room unannounced and hounding her sexually.

Her own mother, though providing no emotional or economic

support, came up from Virginia to pressure her to get rid of the new baby.

"You don't have no job, you have no education and,you don't have no skills," she reasoned. Mother refused, however and continued doing domestic work to provide for herself and me. Soon, her sister Bernice came to Philadelphia to live and work, giving Mother a chance to share a small, one-bedroom apartment which, along with her getting a job as a short-order cook and kitchen worker, improved her lot to some degree.

This was my family background when, at age six, I started public school in Philadelphia. My first day was historic for the wrong reasons. My mother had bought a notebook and pencil for me. But as I stood in the school yard, a brash little girl tried to take my new academic tools from me. I stabbed her in the face with my pencil and was soon facing the principal of the school.

"It is simply not acceptable behavior," he told me, and in retrospect I can explain my behavior much more clearly than I could at age six. I had no family to speak of--no father, no siblings. I had been raised alone and was therefore an anti-social loner. This girl was taking what belonged to me, and I was driven to protect my possessions as best I could.

But I didn't know any of this about myself as I sat in the principal's office listening to him explain how intolerable my behavior was. I was simply afraid, and I felt abandoned. I ran trembling from his office and flew through the streets of Philadelphia without knowing where I was going. My goal was to find my mother. Finally some neighbors found me wandering aimlessly in a nearby park and took me home. That entire first grade experience--my introduction to formal education-- was a struggle for me, primarily because my background had prepared me for absolutely nothing demanding orderliness and propriety.

Meanwhile my mother began a relationship with a man employed by public transportation as an electric trolley car driver, and she lived with him until her death in 1987. In my mind, this second man in her life was no better than my father because he too was abusive--both physically and psychologically. He would get drunk and run through the house like a mad man, tearing up the furniture and punching her.

He also gambled and cursed.

If anything, the memories of the two men in my mother's life have given me a real impetus. Neither was of course representative of Black men in America nor of the typical African-American father in America. However, the lack of positive Black role models is a serious deficit in our community. We Black males in particular who come out of those circumstances must realize the tremendous responsibility that rests on our shoulders, and we therefore must strive to be the fathers to others that our fathers were not to us.

My next discipline problem did not occur until the fourth grade, and it too offers a valuable connection to my central theme.

I had befriended Georgie, a handsome, light-skinned fellow with curly hair.

"Let's go to Woolworth's. I'll buy you some candy," he would offer, and twice or three times weekly he would spend lavishly, treating me to my favorite chocolate bars and small toys. Other times we'd go to the ice cream parlor. I didn't find it difficult to like him, and I marvelled at both the generosity and resources of his father.

But it wasn't generosity. Georgie was stealing one bill at a time from his father's savings which he hid in a can. When confronted, he claimed that I had threatened to beat him up if he did not steal the money.

Suddenly, I was accused of an act the very sound of which was frightening: EXTORTION. Mr. Warner, my teacher summoned my mother to school. Then, miraculously, when Mother arrived, Mr. Warner told her not to whip me because I was a good boy and he believed my version of what had happened. I was not punished by Mother, but was told to stay away from those who would do wrong.

This was the first time that an authority figure supported me in a moment of crisis; it boosted my self-image and helped me to finish the next two years as an above-average student. We all have critical points in our developmental paths that can be either destructive or reinforcing. Here was a critical moment for me of incalculable value, for I was experiencing a quality that is of extreme importance to youngsters: I was being treated fairly.

I graduated from elementary school and was assigned to Shoemaker Junior High. That previous June, the Pearl Street Terrors, an all- girl gang, had stabbed a boy to death in the hallway of the school in a dispute over an umbrella. The news circulated throughout our neighborhood, and the prospect of my attending Shoemaker caused Mother great concern for my safety.

This was also the summer when my grandmother, now in New Jersey, had died. My grandfather was stuck with the responsibility for a wayward high school teenager, my mother's baby sister. So Mother decided to move to Vineland to take care of them--and I'm sure to get me out of Philadelphia.

We moved into Carver Village, the first Black public housing development in Vineland, just before school started. I was enrolled at H.L. Reber Junior High School. There were a number of Black students in the school, but I was the only African American in my seventh-grade class.

As I listened to the Black students raising hell in the classroom down the hallway, I thought that my placement had been a result of our having recently moved to New Jersey and registering late. In fact, I had been placed in that class because of my test scores. This was my first experience with the concept of educational tracking, and frankly, I felt isolated. I remember that my brothers and sisters were having fun and cutting up and not learning while I was being taught how to compete with mainstream students and therefore it seemed, needed to be separated from my people--those who had been somehow judged to be inadequate and behaved accordingly.

Well, the separation continued into the eighth grade but facilitated my being a better than average student who competed favorably with mainstream students. I was elected a class officer, voted best dresser and best dancer, and invited to parties and bar mitzvahs held outside of school.

I didn't enjoy the same popularity with my Black peers. Many of them resented my solid B average and considered me to be a city slicker who had ''too many white friends.'' I remember hearing one critic complain about my ''dancing with white girls.''

Then, proceeding to Vineland High School in the fall of 1954, I experienced another form of educational tracking. This time I was in classes with almost all of the other Black students from H.L. Reber Junior High. What a ball! Instead of being a well-rounded, committed student bent on achieving, I now played and clowned my way through almost two years of high school. My mother complained that my report card had more red and green marks indicating bad conduct and bad grades than the decorations on a Christmas tree.

Yet, as my school performance deteriorated, my acceptance by Black peers grew. I would not be aware for many years of the social injustice of the racial tracking to which we were being subjected. Nor did I have any idea that the courses I was taking were not the only courses that I could enroll in; for me and the rest of my underexposed brothers and sisters, there were no options beyond general math, general English, wood shop and mechanical drawing. We had been placed in an educational ghetto demanding little more that attendance and encouraging irresponsible tomfoolery. Knowing little else, we revelled in our predicament.

So what was I good at? Organized sport had already provided me not only with positive Black male role models but also with opportunities for personal achievement and leadership. I had already quit my guitar lessons so that I could play Little League baseball. I continued in high school. I quarterbacked the undefeated freshman football team and made the varsity wrestling team. This athletic success gave me significant status in school, and everybody knew Ike Tribble as one of Vineland's star athletes capable of forging victories on both the gridiron and the wrestling mat. I had my identity; I knew who I was because my classmates knew who I was and affirmed that identity through their greetings, smiles and slaps on the back.

My greatest ambition was to earn a monogrammed letter, a stately 'V' that I could put on my sweater indicating that I had made the varsity team. So my heart was pumping with pride when I posed with the Monogram Club for the yearbook photograph. It was a defining moment for me to get that letter. I had achieved acceptance and manhood through varsity athletics, and my identity was securely intact.

African-American males today still yearn for that defining moment when their identities are affirmed and they can say unequivocally that they exist. For most Black males, athletics represents the easiest vehicle for this recognition, while military service grows in importance as a measure of manhood. But athletics is far too frequently the only avenue suggested to them. Now I am positive that we must develop ways of encouraging African-American males to define themselves through academic achievement rather than through sports only.

Academics certainly meant little more to me during my first two years at Vineland High School than a means to an end. I had to attend classes in order to compete interscholastically. It was that simple. Of course I know now that continuing on that path of tracked classes and fascination with sports would have been a devastating blow to my life chances. It was a nearly destructive situation, but as I try to emphasize, not irreversible. The odds were against me, but I still had a shot.

It was probably a shot in the dark at first. The word, college was not even in my vocabulary. I knew no African Americans who had gone to college. Nobody in my family had ever mentioned the word. I had never been taught by a Black teacher nor had I been supervised by a Black administrator. Only one Black teacher who taught in elementary school lived in town. College was simply not a concept with which I was familiar.

My mother's guidance and influence had largely been responsible for my performing well academically, for behaving, for being clean and neat, for being respectful of elders including teachers. After I passed the fifth grade, Mother was of little help to me with my homework. But she was a devoted provider of my physical and emotional needs even as hers went lacking. She instituted a reward and sanction structure that included my doing household chores and our going to church every Sunday for fifteen years straight.

She definitely had what we call mother wit. She used tangible rewards to reinforce my good behavior. When I did my chores, I was praised and rewarded with a modest allowance. Although Mother was a domestic who cleaned the homes of white folks, with her meager earnings she furnished me with sports equipment and clothes as well as provided for any of my needs connected with the Boy Scouts or guitar lessons.

The school authorities never consulted my mother about what should be done about my future. She clearly felt that the school knew best, reinforcing the concept of functional interdependence which maintains that institutions are formed and have a life force of their own beyond the individual. She stressed to me the importance of education, questioned the colored marks on my report card, and always admonished me to try harder and to do better. She was convinced that the school system had my best interests at heart.

Now I know that she was typical of what may be called today the powerless underclass. They are dominated and feel intimidated by these critical institutions. Therefore they are not only afraid to but also feel woefully inadequate about challenging them. But what we need more of today are parents who will check on the institutions and hold them responsible, parents who will be totally involved with and fearless of the system.

So I too, at fifteen, believed that adults thought they knew what is best for me although they may not have had any familiarity with my background. In that late afternoon conversation with Mr. Krouse, I was thinking exactly that as he had put aside my transgression with the frog and even encouraged me to achieve against all odds. I would make a mark for my race.

But he did something even more extraordinary than confirm my worth. In one sweeping, definitive, casual sentence, he then told me to go see the counselor the next morning and to tell her that he had said to enroll me in all college prep classes.

College? College prep? What on earth was he talking about? I knew better than to question. The next morning both the counselor and I followed his instructions, and my academic career was never the same.

Without warning, after two years of non-challenging courses, I was studying something called algebra. I had never heard of a math that used letters. Then I was reading *Julius Caesar,* and the idea of literature became a revelation.

My circle of peers changed again once I enrolled in the college track. I was back with the white students who, unlike most of my African-American buddies, had a definite orientation toward the future. For the last two-and-a-half years of high school, I continued as a college prep student and graduated 83rd out of a class of 283, a noteworthy end after a very shaky start.

Maybe it was the Black elementary school teacher. Maybe it was a passing acquaintance. I'm not sure who, but somebody asked me in my senior year if I had thought about going to college.

"No," I answered honestly.

That person told me about an entrance exam for New Jersey state colleges, and suddenly I was in north Jersey for the first time in my life to take the test for admission to Montclair State College.

Now that I had passed and gained admission, how was I to pay for my collegiate experience? My mother had no money. The federal programs now in place were non-existent then, and I had no idea about where to look for financial aid.

Some Black women who worked at the Atlantic City Race Track learned that I was planning to attend college and managed to find a position for me in the maintenance area. I was too young to work there, according to state law. But they knew how badly I needed the money, so they shielded my identity.

It was my first job, that summer of 1958 assignment, and although illegal, it allowed me to save two hundred dollars as I prepared to enter Montclair State College. For the rest of my collegiate life I worked thirty to forty hours a week to pay for my expenses.

My mother's send-off the week before I left for Montclair State was sadly memorable.

She said that she felt bad about not being able to provide me with more tangible support but that she would do her best to send me some spending change when she could. When I seemed to be vacillating or sounded a wee bit discouraged, she looked me in the eye and said, "You are going if you don't stay but a few weeks. You will be the first in our family! Education is something that no one can take away from you." Then she added passionately, "Look at your momma! You don't want to end up like me, cleaning white folk's houses, do you?"

Off I went.

There were only ten Black students out of the 2,200 registered.

I became president of my class for three years, played varsity football, helped to start the wrestling team and wrestled varsity, and belonged to the academic local fraternity, Phi Alpha Psi. My formal education may have begun with me wandering aimlessly away from the first grade, but it progressed to where I was able to leave college with a focused sense of purpose and a job of which I was proud.

Where one begins does not have to determine where one ends up. Out of adversity comes strength, and often, what appears to offer little direction ends up providing the necessary seeds for one's own personal harvest.

There are a million stories like mine. I am certain that many of them would make mine seem as if I had grown up with a silver spoon in my mouth. For me the critical difference was Mr. Krouse, who believed that where I came from was not where I was going. And since I was not brain damaged, I could learn.

3

Do Not Call the Forest That Shelters You a Jungle

Although there is a substantial amount of documentation about the African-American past, this history has only recently been examined properly by scholars. Despite this more honest appraisal however, not enough has been done to incorporate Black history into the classrooms of America's schools and colleges. The achievements and contributions of African Americans and other minorities are rarely mentioned in the curriculum of many schools, (Appleton, 1982). Accordingly, African-American history courses remain apart from the mandatory curriculum at most schools, with only a small number of minority students and even fewer majority students enrolling in these courses.

I believe that this lack of appreciation for and sharing of African-American history and culture has impeded the progress of Blacks in America by depriving African Americans--particularly our youth--of inspiring images, of motivating achievements, and of nurturing wisdom. Without the awareness of our priceless heritage, we African Americans are stuck with an uncertain destiny in America. It only takes a little wisdom to realize that people "who do not know from whence they have come, cannot know where they may be going." Uniquely, African Americans are victims of a tradition disrupted--of a glorious past that has been interrupted, suppressed and denied. Ironically, other Americans are also victimized by this suppression and denial of the African-American past, for without the knowledge and understanding of how this history has affected current African-American progress and majority attitudes, American citizens are both the creators and indirectly the victims of racism in America.

Focusing on three distinctly relevant parts of our history, I hope to provide some foundation for understanding the consequences of denying Black America's heritage. First my look at the past begins with the African experience. Next, I describe the introduction of Africans as slaves in the New World colonies--an introduction which developed into the institution of slavery and which gave birth to the sharecropping system. Thirdly, I discuss the "Great Migration" of African Americans to the North that provided the human chattel for the development of urban ghettos.

I hope in this historical overview to help explode the myths which have provided the basis for so much racist stereotyping in America about African Americans being innately lazy, ignorant and hedonistic. At the same time, The stage will be set for a better understanding of not only the current status of the African-American community, but also of what must be done to eradicate American racism based on the fiction of Black inferiority. Finally, by reflecting on this past, I want to suggest new directions for further developing human potential and for creating a cohesive group achievement culture for African Americans.

History of Africa

World history classes, until recently, discussed Africa as the Dark Continent, inhabited by mindless natives in loin cloths, throwing spears at friend and foe alike. False images of a place with no government, culture, education, or other *accoutrements* of civilization were created. In these same world history classes, however, Egypt was discussed as the "cradle of civilization" to which the foundations of much of science, mathematics, and culture were attributed and could be traced. Egypt was heralded as a country of such splendor while the Dark Continent was essentially written off as a cultural wasteland because the historians continually denied the Black African influences of Egyptian tradition (Wrigley, 1971).

The splitting of Africa and Egypt into two distinct cultures, when in fact they overlap, is a direct result of the institutional racism that permeates the worlds of university scholarship, public school education and textbook publishing. Asa Hilliard (1987) suggests that historians had to account for the obvious contradiction that developed during the great archaeological discoveries taking place in Africa *which included Egypt.* These discoveries occurred at the same time that European governments were dividing up the spoils of Africa. The discrepancy between the undeniably great civilization of the Nile on the one hand and the concocted theories of racial inferiority used to justify slavery on the other became so obvious that historians were forced into developing yet another theory to protect the interests of those already billing Africa as the continent of savages. This theory relied upon a dichotomy that falsely distinguished Egyptians, who historians claim were white but browned by the sun, and Africans, who were born black. In this way, by setting up this Black African-Egyptian dichotomy, historians were able to perpetuate existing myths about the limited abilities of Blacks.

Public schools and textbook publishers supplying these institutions, moreover, did not question the so-called historical experts. Such a portrayal of Black Africans as savage brutes was, at best, wrong and, at worst, verification of an insolently inaccurate portrayal of the African-American homeland--a portrayal which to this day still retards the African-American community's respect and self-esteem.

Despite the fact that this false portrayal of Black Africans largely has been erased from world history texts, many noteworthy facts concerning Black African history that could champion an accurate and positive view of the African-American homeland and augment African-American respect and self-esteem are still seldom discussed in contemporary books about world history or cultural heritage (Appleton, 1983).

In my talks with young African Americans around the country, I tend to emphasize the history of three great African centers as well as the overlooked contributions of Egyptians when I review the importance of understanding our heritage.

Often overlooked or ignored, for example, is evidence that between the eighth and sixteenth centuries, three great Black African countries, Ghana, Mali and Songhay flourished as centers of government, education and culture. Records show that Ghana, West Africa's first state, flourished in the eleventh century under the reign of Tenkamenin. Trade was a central component of Ghana's economy, and it exported commodities like rubber, ivory, and gold in exchange for wheat, fruit, textiles, brass, and salt. Additionally, the country had established a government hierarchy as well as a national religion (Bennett, 1987).

Mali replaced Ghana as the center of commerce and culture by the end of the eleventh century and maintained this status well into the twelfth century. Documented pilgrimages by the kings of Mali to Mecca, spiritual center of Islam, provide insight into the extent of the wealth and resources of Mali. One of these pilgrimages by King Gonga-Musa included an entourage of 60,000 people including military escorts and servants. During the reigns of Gonga-Musa and his successor, Suleiman, Mali enjoyed international trade relations, a state religion, and a flourishing educational system. The country remained a leader of African nations until the fifteenth century when aggressions by the peoples of Songhay and Mossi, as well as infiltration by the Portuguese, brought the country to a condition of disrepair and decline (Bennett, 1987).

Songhay was developed as a nation as early as the beginning of the eighth century. It did not emerge as one of the great nations of the Sudan, however, until the latter part of the fifteenth century under the rulers Sonni Ali and Askia Mohammed. During Sonni Ali's reign, the great cities of Timbuktu and Jenne were incorporated into Songhay.

Under King Askia's rule, Songhay prospered from international trade, and it instituted banking and credit systems as well as sales inspections and a system of weights and measures. King Askia also placed importance on education; it was during his reign that the cities of Gao, Walata, Timbuktu, and Jenne developed as intellectual centers. Scholars, both from Asia and Europe alike, came to the universities in these cities to study grammar, geography, law, literature, surgery, and Islam. The robust health of scholarship in these cities is substantiated by reports that the book trade of Timbuktu brought in more money than any other commodity (Bennett, 1987).

Furthermore, the contributions of Egyptians (who are Africans) to mathematics, for example, deserve the special consideration they too often fail to find. The Great Pyramids are a prime example of the conceptual talents, in addition to the engineering and organizational ingenuity, of Africans. The formulas and calculations used in designing the pyramids were based on original concepts of spatial and numerical relationships, and their continued existence is testimony to the understanding and mastery of calculus and geometry that the African designers had achieved well before their European counterparts.

These brief glimpses into the achievements of great African societies provide irrefutable evidence that Africans as a people prized culture, supported formal education and produced valuable scholarship; they were not mere savage brutes. So the whole notion that African Americans are kin to some second-class race and are devoid of any sense of communal respect and self-esteem is not only folly but also is inconsistent with historical evidence.

Familiarizing all Americans with the contributions of these three African societies including Egypt could challenge old stereotypes about the limited abilities of African Americans. Further, we could establish positive, historical role models for African-American children and eradicate false myths from American culture. Knowing about these contributions, for example, to the technical fields of science, mathematics, and engineering by Africans can be an empowering incentive for Blacks. And these contributions can earn the respect of whites. The time for this knowledge--given the powerlessness and despair which gnaw at many African Americans as a result of the negative images once provided by too many textbooks and media representations--is now. I believe that knowledge can mobilize the masses and that the truth about the history and accomplishments of African Americans will motivate the masses to reexamine their common heritage and discard the baggage of centuries of misinformation.

European Slave Trade

During the 1400's, Portugal, France, Spain and later Holland invaded the continent of Africa in search of expanding commercial interests. African slaves, in addition to other commodities such as nuts, fruit, olive oil, and gold were sold by the Europeans as early as the middle of the fifteenth century. Historian John Hope Franklin notes that while all the mechanisms were in place by the end of the fifteenth century to support the European slave trade, no profitable future existed for slavery in Europe. Simply stated, there was an insufficient number of jobs in Europe's banks, shipyards, mercantile establishments, and homes of the wealthy to make the slave trade a profitable endeavor (Franklin, 1967).

The settlement of the New World, however, radically changed the profit factor of the African slave trade. By the seventeenth century, the European colonies were in dire need of a labor supply to support their burgeoning farming endeavors. Initially, Indians and then poor Europeans were used as a labor supply, but neither of these groups was a continuing, satisfactory source. Then in 1517, Bishop Las Casas advocated allowing each immigrating Spaniard to import twelve Africans, and the African slave trade to the New World had begun in earnest (Franklin, 1967).

The Portuguese were actually the first to bring African slaves to the New World, but they did not dominate the commercial exploitation of slave trading. It was the Dutch, French, and English who aggressively commanded significant parts of this lucrative trade. During the fifteenth century, Holland profited the most from the African slave trade; during the sixteenth century the French and

English replaced the Dutch as leaders in the trading of slaves to the New World. By the eighteenth century, the African slave trade was such a significant part of the British economic system that British slave traders provided not only the British colonies with slaves, but virtually all the colonies regardless of their national allegiances.

Accurate estimates of the number of slaves forced to North and South America from the sixteenth to the nineteenth centuries are unavailable because of poor or non-existent record-keeping. But as many as fifteen million Africans are estimated to have been forced from their homeland during this time. The consequences of this violent, forced departure from home were felt not only by future generations of African Americans, but also by Africans in their homeland. Robbed of many of their strongest, most able males and females, Africans experienced a recession of spirit, culture, and economy which continued as a function of further exploitation and subsequent invasions from European nations during the nineteenth century.

The treatment of the African slaves varied tremendously depending upon their final destination. In South America where the Catholic Church was a dominating social and moral force, Africans who came as slaves were typically considered humans with souls to be saved. In contrast, most North Americans viewed African slaves as creatures without souls or human spirits. The contemporary tranquility between peoples of color in South America, in contrast to the continuing tensions between the races which exist in North America may very well be traced back to these antithetical historical perceptions of Africans as either humans or beasts, with or without souls.

The Slavery Process

Africans were taken to the West Indies to be "seasoned," or taught the expected ways of slave life after being captured but before being sold. Franklin estimates that during the seasoning period, generally lasting three or four years, the newly enslaved Africans suffered a thirty percent mortality rate (Franklin, 1967). Illness, adjustment to a new climate and culture, excessive hours of work, inadequate food, suicide, loss of family, home, and country, as well as the brutal practices of the overseers were all contributors to this high mortality rate. For those Africans who survived, seasoning served to further strip them of their language, culture, religion, and independence of mind and body. Africans, therefore left the West Indies and travelled to North America in a disoriented and disheartened state.

The enslavement of Africans by North American plantation owners was the next tragic step for those slaves surviving seasoning. Inhumane treatment of Africans was commonplace on these plantations since plantation owners were not concerned about the physical or mental health of the African slaves. The religious and emotional needs of slaves were also ignored. They experienced harsh working conditions and frequent separation of friend, kin and makeshift family members as consequences of being bought and sold by different "buyers." These conditions, coupled with the suppression of African language and culture and the successful disorientation wrought by seasoning, made it almost impossible for African Americans to develop any consistent sense of community.

Still, despite the multitude of hardships faced by African Americans, examples of individual achievement did exist during the plantation period: Phyllis Wheatley, a Black slave whose collection of poems was published in 1773 and entitled *Poems; on Various Subjects, Religions and Moral*, was established as America's first prominent Black female poet; Benjamin Banneker, a self-educated free Black, was invited by President George Washington to help survey the grounds for the nation's Capitol, and Frederick Douglass, an escaped slave who served as a consultant to President Lincoln during the Civil War, was a leading nineteenth century human rights activist who held government appointments including U.S. Minister and Counsel General to Haiti from 1889-1891. These individuals all established themselves as outstanding contributors to the literary, intellectual and political world of their day and their individual achievements confirm the inaccuracy of the myth that African Americans are innately unable to learn or achieve.

Despite these achievements by individuals, no opportunities existed for group achievement, group identification, or group solidarity among displaced African Americans. Slaves were, quite literally, at the total mercy of the plantation owners. Few, if any, laws existed to protect the rights of slaves, and in fact, social conditions were structured to prevent any kind of group progress from being made by the slaves. These oppressive social and legal conditions obliterated human dignity for African Americans as a group; slaves for the most part were bonded only by the dehumanizing slavery system.

The African enslavement process, in a word, was brutal. Many Africans died in the overcrowded and unhygienic conditions that existed on the slave ships taking them from their homeland. Many more died trying to escape from their brutal captors. A search of the Atlantic Ocean would no doubt reveal the skeletons of tens of thousands of captured Africans who died and were tossed overboard on their way to the New World. Those Africans who died resisting capture in Africa, those who died fighting captivity aboard ship, those who died while being seasoned and those who, along with their children and children's children, died resisting the slavery system easily exceed twenty million lives lost (Rathbone, 1985).

The Emancipation Proclamation

Lincoln's signature on the *Emancipation Proclamation* on January 1, 1863 emancipated more than three-fourths of all slaves in the United States. Although it legally destroyed slavery, the proclamation was not the end of the exploitation and oppression of African Americans. In fact, it is important to note that Lincoln freed slaves in geographic areas not under his control and left those in bondage in areas still under federal control.

The Reconstruction era that followed the emancipation was a time of emotional and physical re-building for African Americans. The Freedmen's Bureau aided former slaves by furnishing them with supplies and medical services and, most importantly, by establishing Black schools, colleges, and universities. Howard University, Hampton Institute, St. Augustine's College, Atlanta University, Fisk University and Storer College are some of the institutions of higher education founded with the assistance of the bureau. The American

Missionary Association, Baptists, Methodists, Presbyterians, and Episcopalians also assumed vital roles in the support of schools, colleges, and universities for African Americans.

By 1870 records show that 247,333 pupils were enrolled in one of 4,329 schools initiated by the Freedmen's Bureau (Franklin, 1967). This work, plus the progress made by African Americans since the establishment of these schools, a short 125 years ago, should certainly dispel all racist assumptions about the motivation and abilities of African- Americans to be active learners contributing to society.

But oppression and racism did not end with Reconstruction. In the South, slavery was replaced by yet another restrictive, punishing economic institution. For many unskilled and uneducated African Americans, sharecropping provided the most viable option for subsistence although the opportunity existed to go North into uncertainty. Under the sharecropping system, a family worked the fields and was compensated by the owner of the land with a significant percentage of the crops. This system provided the labor necessary for plantation owners to have all of their lands farmed. Sharecropping for African-American families was, to a large extent, just a continuation of slavery since social and economic independence was impossible for them as a group to achieve. Without economic independence, spiritual and cultural independence remained difficult, if not impossible, to establish and maintain. To be sure, although legally free, sharecroppers still did not enjoy the freedom of simple social discourse or of educational opportunities because of their almost total dependence on the landowners. Sharecropping in the South was another chapter in the continuing drama of African Americans' becoming an oppressed group within the American Anglo-Saxon social fabric.

The Great Migration

The Great Migration of Southern African Americans to the urban North represents the next chapter of this continuing saga involving the oppression of African Americans in the United States. While the setting changed from agrarian South to urban North, the dependency status of African Americans continued. The urban ghetto continued to limit their educational and cultural opportunities, and metropolitan factories provided no relief from economic dependence. Housing was a particular problem in the urban areas as segregated residential policies were developed. Overcrowding and sub-standard housing was common as landlords, usually Caucasian like their counterparts on the plantation, exploited African Americans. Once again, African Americans were forced to live in environmental conditions which were emotionally and economically debilitating. Educational opportunities and successes were also infrequent phenomena in the urban ghettos. The only positive result of this urban predicament was that all levels of the African-American social order lived in these ghettos together. Consequently, some Black role models were created, and a form of upward mobility which somewhat lessened hopelessness took shape.

But our families suffered. The disintegration of the African-American family, an already tenuous institution due to two hundred and fifty years of slavery, was now even more difficult to avoid as Blacks struggled to cope with yet another new social setting. Employment opportunities in the North were particularly difficult for African-American men who were not welcomed by the labor unions. African-American women had an easier time finding employment, but, of course, opportunities were restricted mostly to positions as household servants and other low-skill positions. Similar to the environments of slavery and sharecropping, the urban ghetto too subjugated Blacks. How then, could group identity, achievement, and pride under such severe conditions find an outlet? The achievement of these goals still remains an all too distant reality today for the African-American community; and the dimness of the prospects is a direct consequence of a tradition disrupted.

References

Appleton, N. (1983). *Cultural Pluralism in Education: Theoretical Foundations.* New York: Longman.

Bennett, L. (1987). *Before The Mayflower: A History of Black America.* (6th Edition). Chicago: Johnson Publishing Company.

Franklin, J.H. (1967). *From Slavery to Freedom: A History of Negro Americans.* New York: Vintage Books.

Hilliard, A. (1987). *Baseline Essays.* Portland School District.

Rathbone, R. (1985). Some thoughts on resistance to enslavement in West Africa. *Slavery and Abolition* (Great Britain), 6 (3), 11- 23.

Wrigley, C.C. (1971). Historicism in Africa: slavery and state formation. *African Affairs* (Great Britain), 70 (279), 113-124.

4

You Can't Build a House for Last Year's Summer

African-American children in this country's public education system have failed at a rate that is disproportionately high despite the fact that a host of programs over the last three decades have been designed to improve the academic performance of our youth. These efforts have been in the main unsuccessful. In order to appreciate the new directions and new models that I am proposing to reverse these trends, it is necessary to identify the barriers which have prevented Black children from succeeding.

What I hope to show is that the failure to bring about any change in the achievement levels of our youth is a result of these programs' refusing to develop strategies that attack and overhaul the root cause of this academic faltering. Essentially, the issue is that oppressive social conditions under which most African-American children languish daily must be addressed before academic performance can be improved measurably.

Accordingly, the various avenues taken in the past have not sufficiently addressed the need to change the school environments so that they are more conducive to academic success for African-American children. These changes, which I think are necessary, recognize the wisdom of the African proverb: You can't build a house for last year's summer.

Academic Performance Examined

But let me point out some key features of the failure of Black children to achieve. First, it is a phenomenon that is quite real and quite consistent. And just as important, the causes of this failure have not been identified correctly.

By poor performance, I mean that consistently, when you look at the statistics, you see that Black youth are at the bottom of the scale when the relevant categories like completion rates, college-going rates, and test scores are examined. In addition, African-American youth tend to be suspended and expelled at frequencies much greater than those for majority students. Finally, their enrollments in classes for the gifted are low while enrollments in classes for the so-called learning disabled are high.

We know too, that this historical pattern of failure on the part of African-American children as compared to their majority counterparts persists regardless of where the school is located (Washington and LaPoint, 1988).

Whether Black children are placed in de facto or de jure segregated schools or in integrated schools "up North," "down South" or points in between, poor academic performances mirror one another.

Examples do exist which suggest that when Black children and majority children share a relatively high socioeconomic status and middle-class environment, their academic performance records are similar. However, African-American children who are included in the middle or upper class represent a distinct minority. Further, there is little hope for significant movement of more Blacks into these classes where the conditions for high academic achievement best exist.

Census Bureau projections suggest that by the year 2000, African-American women and children will represent the majority of the women and children who will fall below the federally defined poverty line. The few middle-class Black children who will experience favorable conditions for academic success and who will consequently be more likely to perform well in school are insufficient in number to have much effect on the performance of the total group.

So neither changing the school setting nor hoping to improve the socioeconomic status of Black families represents much of an answer.

What we need is a strategy that breaks down the two major barriers: cultural isolation on the one hand, and the double standard involved in the academic labeling process on the other.

Both of these barriers, using the public school system as their foundation, have helped to institutionalize racism (Knowles & Pruitt, 1969).

The first barrier to academic achievement, isolation from cultural roots, can result in both psychological and emotional harm to Black children. This damage is manifested in identity crises, confusion, and insecurity--neither of which is conducive to competing for academic success.

Furthermore, the second barrier, the use of a double standard by school personnel in the academic labeling process, all too often results in African-American children being designated as behavior problems despite the fact that their conduct and academic potential are similar to those of their majority classmates. This double standard or labeling, which is consciously or unconsciously motivated by ignorance and racial stereotyping, finally lowers the expectations that school person-nel (usually middle- and upper-class whites) have of Black young-sters. Consequently proper nurturing and guidance of our Black youth does not take place.

Rather than being encouraged to pursue academic or college preparatory courses, these youngsters are instead placed into voca-tional tracks. The inadequacies of this approach are obvious: They are poorly prepared for continuing education, have acquired little knowl-edge and have seen their self-esteem lowered considerably. So the likelihood of their achieving academic success and a higher socioeconomic status in the future is diminished. This is how institutional racism can prevent even the socially privileged African-American children from enjoying the same opportunities as majority students. Regardless of class or background, African-American children confront a difficult time in reaching their full potential in American schools as they are presently operated.

Nature vs. Nurture

Historically, when educators have examined the poor educational learning experiences of African-American children in the public schools, they have come to one of two conclusions. The first, which will not be explored for obvious reasons, is that the unimpressive academic performance record of Blacks is a consequence of genetic inferiority. Proponents of this view have claimed that African Americans are incapable of high academic achievement because of our small brain size, our low intellectual ability and our cultural deprivation (Watson, 1973).

The second conclusion, which directly opposes the first, is that the poor performance of African-American children in school is the product of a plethora of adverse environmental conditions.

Proponents of this second view, which I call the environmental perspective, conclude that socioeconomic status, family support and a nurturing environment are the conditions necessary among African-American children for competitive academic achievement (Hill, 1972). This perspective suggests that these children will achieve as well as their majority counterparts if they are simply provided with an environment conducive to learning and achieving. Unfortunately, those who support this view fail to recognize the crux of the matter: that the ability of all African Americans to achieve in academic settings, regardless of their socioeconomic status, is affected by historical antecedents and the continuing racist nature of both the American public school system and the larger society.

As the historical overview provided in Chapter Two illustrates, African Americans have had their cultural tradition, including a strong educational and family orientation, drastically disrupted during the period of the European slave trade. This historical interruption is a key environmental factor which has persisted and has clearly proved to be highly detrimental to the present academic success and overall well-being of African Americans.

Since their arrival in the New World in Jamestown, Virginia in 1619, African Americans have continually had to combat socioeconomic injustice supported by discriminatory practices and legal enactments (Jordan, 1962). And as they progressed historically from slavery to sharecropping to the urban ghettoes of the North, the upheaval has caused tremendous social stigma and psychological pain. These experiences at best have provided weak and incomplete foundations for establishing and nurturing the secure homes with supportive learning environments that educators insist we must have. Moreover, our experiences have prevented African Americans from gaining the proper knowledge and designing the clear blueprints for utilizing whatever resources and political influence that we may have access to today.

So the inferior performance of Black children in contrast to the achievement of their majority counterparts clearly reflects the different histories of their respective peoples. There is little denial even among the most racist of Americans that a person's past is a significant determinant of his or her future. Does it not follow therefore that an understanding of the academic achievement of African-American children lies in the understanding of their history and not in the researching of their genes?

Society Responds: the 1960's

But the programs set up to improve the educational achievement of African Americans during the last several decades have focused on areas that were not germane to these issues of cultural isolation and labeling.

In fact, the drive in the 1950's for equal access to educational and other opportunities for all Americans was sparked by the belief in the relationship between education and economic status. This neo-classical economic perspective said that improving the educational attainment of African Americans would directly result in their improved individual economic status as well as in their improved productivity in the work force.

So America began in the 1950's to address its historical patterns of racial inequality, and the attacks on this system became the primary targets of the early civil rights movement. Finally, in 1954, the Supreme Court ruled in *Brown vs. Board of Education of Topeka* that ''separate but equal'' schools were unconstitutional since they maintained segregation and discriminated against African Americans as a class. A series of court cases contesting segregation in the public schools followed the Brown decision, and the NAACP and other Black civil rights groups fought vigorously for equities long denied Black Americans.

Suddenly, and in large measure as a consequence of the civil rights movement, the African-American family became a focus of great interest. The ''war on poverty'' was initiated during the 1960's to combat and change many of the prevailing conditions experienced by the Black family.

One focus of the war on poverty was to improve the educational opportunities for African-American youngsters. And it was here that well-meaning efforts resulted, ironically, in psychologically and socially damaging consequences. Our African-American children were labelled in various ways in an attempt to describe and remedy the academic needs of this special population. Identifications placed on them during this period included ''culturally deprived,'' ''socially disadvantaged,'' ''cognitively deficient,'' and ''victims of a cycle of poverty.''

If anything, the prevailing philosophy behind the war was that first the government would tell the group that it was deficient, and then the government would fix the deficiency. It was almost as if Mr. Krouse had told me back in high school that my lowly background was indeed a hindrance to my potential and that I should not have felt stigmatized by his assessment.

In an effort to begin changing the predictable patterns of low achievement and poor educational outcomes of African-American children, Congress passed the Elementary and Secondary Education Act (ESEA) in 1964. ESEA represented a long-term commitment of federal funding for local schools in an effort to reduce the educational gap between African-American and majority youngsters. By providing the public schools with programmatic direction and funding, Congress, via ESEA, hoped to alter historical patterns of poor educational performance. This federal mandate and commitment to addressing past inequities accurately captured the egalitarian spirit which prevailed in federal public policy-making throughout the 1960's.

This environment of government as an assertive agent of change, however, did not continue much beyond the 1960's. In fact, thirty five years and billions of dollars later, it is not an overstatement that the public education system is no closer to improving the performance of either African Americans in the aggregate or other socially disadvantaged minorities. Identifiable performance measures are not significantly different from those at the time when Congress first mandated the dedication of federal funds to address the problem.

I am neither condemning these past efforts, nor merely offering a neo-conservative analysis of the current status of African-American academic achievement in the United States. Rather, I am affirming that money alone is an insufficient mechanism for addressing the systemic and endemic conditions which the vast majority of African Americans confront on a daily basis. What clearly is needed is a better understanding, along with a major overhaul, of strategies by which oppressive social conditions can be addressed. This understanding can help produce programs which would extend far beyond the Band-Aid approaches attempted since the fifties.

Additionally, professional educators and policy-makers need an action agenda to deal with not only the situations which confront the African-American community but also the impact that these situations have on the education of the community's children.

The initiatives undertaken and promoted during the sixties by national, and to some extent, state and local education policy-makers revolved around rudimentary and superficial changes in the school environments. Efforts such as brief in-service training sessions to improve teachers' sensitivity to African-American and other minority students were, if not mockeries of the complexity of the issue, cursory and certainly too meager to promote understanding or sizable behavioral changes in the school setting.

Curriculum changes were made in some school districts, but for the most part they were limited to adding a single course in Black history to the curriculum. While a welcome addition to the classroom, a single course in Black history also represented a quick fix to change. Still lacking was the correction, expansion, and modification of courses in all content areas, most notably in the sciences and social sciences. These are the areas which fail to include the African influences on American society as well as the contributions made in the United States and the world by African Americans and other minorities, including women (Appleton, 1983).

Unfortunately, most schools continue to present only Western European influences on American culture and history as if they represent the only cultural lineage of the majority group in America. Even when confronted with this skewed view of American history, educators typically insist that the treatment of African Americans in contemporary U.S. history books is adequate (Garcia & Goebel, 1985). By promoting such ethnocentrism, the schools act to maintain and protect the existing status quo of Anglo-Saxon America at the cost of denying all minority students pride in their cultural heritage and diversity.

This is the result of billions of dollars of federal assistance to fund special programs such as Head Start, and Title I. Even though they have achieved some measurable success, they are shackled from being greater than they are because of their systematic delivery of ''Waspish'' culture and history.

As a consequence, American schools continue to produce in the main, low-achieving minority children; African-American youngsters continue to march to the beat of majority drums and remain out-of-step with the rhythm for academic success.

The Rebirth of Meritocracy: the 1970's and 1980's

These commitments made in the early 1960's to addressing inequities in the education of African Americans began to diminish late in that decade. The mood of enthusiasm and high hopes that concerned professionals and parents had about the possibility of the federal government's promoting change soon dimmed to pessimism. As we moved from the late 1960's to the 1970's, the dominant political spirit--orchestrated by the conservative right--could be described as one of waning expectations highlighted by a return to the ideal of meritocracy. The climate which promoted an egalitarian society advocating equal rights for all citizens--and which had been reflected in progressive public policies--came to an abrupt close first with the election of Richard M. Nixon in 1968 and secondly with the rise of Ronald Reagan as a viable national candidate during the 1970's. Any commitment to equal access to opportunity for minorities was killed, at least temporarily, by the 1980 presidential election of Ronald Reagan.

The conservative right's priority on excellence as defined by new measurable performance standards has been contradictory at best to notions of equal access and opportunity; certainly it has drawn a false dichotomy between excellence and equity.

During this return to meritocracy, programs and other policy initiatives addressing the special needs of America's minority populations--programs promoted by former administrations--have suffered dramatic budget cuts and a continued assault from the political right. Nonetheless, it is clearer today than ever before that excellence cannot be achieved in American schools without equity and access for all Americans.

Responding to these federal funding cuts, proponents of equal opportunity programs and related initiatives have been forced to review past actions and to redirect their efforts. In this redirection, approaches have been developed which lessen the dependency on federal funds and shift the responsibility and control to the states, their local communities and private sources. Indeed, the new necessary question for citizens concerned about creating viable educational opportunities for African-American youngsters is what initiatives can be implemented in this age of federal retrenchment which will accomplish what seemingly limitless budgets and a supportive political environment could not accomplish in the 1960's.

The answer is even more complex and urgently needed when placed in the context of the re-emergence of meritocratic principles in America. These principles, focusing on examinations, standards and other measurable qualities of value, are important components of the 1980's movement for reform in public education.

For example, the National Commission on Excellence in Education (1983), the most visible of the plethora of reports directing public policy makers toward the "shoring up" of the educational delivery system, presents "standards and expectations" as its first area of discussion. In this new era of reform, therefore, the urgency of providing access and excellence to America's African-American youngsters needs to be understood by all who are concerned about the current and future status of African Americans and the society.

The Education Reform Movement of the 1980's

Virtually every state had placed educational reform on legislative and educational agendas by the mid-1980's. Michael Kirst at Stanford University notes that this period of reform has dramatically altered the governance of public education in grades K-12. No longer are virtually all school policies and decisions made at the local level; states are increasingly making decisions which guide, if not mandate, local school policies.

The Florida Legislature, for example, notably during the eight-year administration of Governor Bob Graham (1978-1986), pushed for initiatives that included, but were not limited to, more rigorous state-wide high school graduation requirements, an increase in the number of school hours, new teaching requirements for public school teachers and an increase in admission standards for the state university system.

It seemed as if we had moved from a question of access to one of excess. Indeed, to many African-American leaders and other progressive groups, the problems which accompanied those policies designed to ensure educational access in the 1960's had now changed to problems related to questions of excess by the 1980's: liberal admission policies which allowed many Black students into colleges and universities who were ''not qualified'' according to previously rigid and restrictive standards during the 1960's and into the 1970's were now considered excesses as part of the thrust for excellence.

Statewide testing programs and stiffer criteria for admission and retention have effectively screened out some of these so-called lesser-qualified individuals from the public education system. So in the final analysis, the so-called thrust for excellence has been diametrically opposed to the hard-fought battles to ensure access and equity for African Americans. The new, continued drive for excellence coupled with the focus on higher standards, in general, does not bode well for socially disadvantaged minority students (Swift, 1986).

Despite the federal government's making the question of equity less of a federal priority at the K-12 level in the 1980's, some progress can be reported on African-American participation in higher education nevertheless. By the mid-seventies, more than a million Black students, a figure higher than at any time in this country's history, were attending postsecondary institutions (U.S. Bureau of Census, 1976).

However, when we analyze the fields of study that were selected by these students along with their retention and completion rates compared to majority counterparts, we encounter additional evidence that Black students continue to face institutional racism along with other social and economic barriers which make the accomplishment of the baccalaureate degree a more difficult task for them than for the majority (Smith, Simpson-Kirkland, Zimmern, Goldstein & Prichard, 1986). The students were clustered in education, social sciences and increasingly in business. There were no significant increases in the fields of science and technology. Further, their completion and retention rates are significantly lower that those of majority students.

Other statistics support the view that institutional racism is a major deterrent to Black student achievement. For example, 43% of African-American students, as opposed to 36% of majority students, begin their postsecondary careers in the community college setting (Wilson,

1988). Kenneth Clarke (1960) recognized long ago that community colleges serve as a screening agent to ''cool out'' some students by lowering their aspirations to achieve the baccalaureate degree. Karabel (1972) expands Clarke's construct of ''cooling out'' and concludes that community colleges serve as social stratification agents by lowering the aspirations of groups with certain racial or socioeconomic characteristics to achieve a four-year degree.

As reported in *The Chronicle of Higher Education* (1986), some community colleges continue to cool out or lower the aspirations of minority students, even when these students cite transferring to a senior institution as their primary academic goal. Through career counseling, community college officials often redirect the academic programs of minority students, notably African Americans, to vocational programs. Consequently, many of these students will not successfully matriculate to four-year senior institutions. For those who can fight institutional racism and matriculate to four-year institutions, the probability of graduating is significantly less than it is for their African-American and majority counterparts who began their collegiate careers at four-year institutions. African-American students who begin college at four-year institutions have higher retention and graduation rates than transfer students.

At the primary and secondary levels of education, similarly bleak statistics suggest that African-American children have markedly different and less successful educational experiences than their majority counterparts. Disproportionate numbers of Black students are placed in classes for the educationally handicapped (Washington & LaPoint, 1988). Similarly, these students are more likely to receive both corporal punishment, suspensions and expulsions from schools than their majority counterparts.

These facts help substantiate the contention that pre-college education is not producing an adequate number of prepared students to continue beyond postsecondary education. Without such a pipeline which results in a qualified student pool for advanced studies, the late eighties and early nineties will see a continued decrease in African-American participation (The College Board, 1985).

This pipeline will never be populated adequately, however, until the school environments are changed so that they are no longer failing the failed. The premises behind the old programs will not work. You can't build a house for last year's summer.

References

Appleton, N. (1983). *Cultural Pluralism in Education: Theoretical Foundations*. Longman: New York.

Clarke, K. (1965). *Dark Ghetto: Dilemmas of Social Power*. (1st ed.). New York: Harper & Row.

College Board. (1985). Equality and Excellence. *The Educational Status of Black Americans*. New York: The College Board.

Garcia, J., & Goebel, J. (1985). A comparative study of the portrayal of Black Americans in selected U.S. textbooks. *The Negro Education Review*. 36 (4), 118-127.

Hill, R. (1972). *The Strength of Black Families*. New York: Emerson Hall.

Jordan, W.D. (1968). *White over Black: American Attitudes Toward the Negro, 1550-1812*. Chapel Hill: University of North Carolina Press.

Karabel, J., & Halsey, A.H. (Eds.). *Power and Ideology in Education*. New York: Oxford University Press.

Knowles, L., & Pruitt, K., (1969). *Institutional Racism in America*. Englewood Cliffs: Prentice-Hall.

Ogbu, J. U. (1988). Black Education: A cultural-ecological perspective. In H.P. McAdoo (Ed.)., *Black Families* (2nd Ed.) (pp. 169-184). Newbury Park, CA: Sage.

Smith, Simpson-Kirkland, Zimmern, Goldstein & Prichard. (1986, April). The five most important problems confronting black students today. *The Negro Education Review*, 37 (2) 52-61.

Swift, J.S., Jr., (1986). The move to educational excellence does not mean a move to educational equality. *The Negro Educational Review*, 36 (3-4), 119-126.

Washington, V., & OaPoint, V. (1988). *Black Children and American Institutions: An Ecological Review and Resource Guide.* New York: Garland.

Watson, B.C. (1973). *Stupidity, Sloth, and Public Policy: Social Darwinism Rides Again.* National Urban Coalition.

Wilson, R. & Carter, D.J. (1988). *Minorities in Higher Education.* American Council on Education.

5

Unless You Call Out, Who Will Open the Door?

W hat kind of change is necessary and what are the essential components? How do we need to proceed to improve the academic performance of Black youngsters in the aggregate? What part of the system needs to be addressed first?

In order for change to be worthwhile and meaningful, educators must begin to resolve the contradictions inherent in the public school system's mission of transmitting only one select brand of American culture.

But before facing this challenge of cultural inclusion directly, it will be necessary to comment on what may be termed the societal roles of the public school system.

Public schools have long been recognized as serving the needs of society other than the mere teaching of reading, writing, and arithmetic to youngsters. To illustrate, during the massive waves of immigration at the turn of the twentieth century, our schools were viewed as the primary institution that would help transform immigrants and their offspring from being foreigners to being Americans; the schools served as the accepted ''melting pots'' of different cultures and backgrounds and became one of the prime socializing agents for achieving the American dream of success.

Despite federal legislation such as the Elementary and Secondary Education Act (1965), of which Title I was a central feature and which was directed at making public schools more reflective of all cultures, these schools have continued to embrace the basic values, attitudes, and mores of the European immigrants to the near exclusion of those basic values, attitudes, and mores of other immigrant groups.

African Americans in particular have never had their cultural values or human needs represented within the fabric of the public schools. The failure of the public schools to embrace specifically African-American cultural values and precepts is directly related to the perennially discriminatory treatment that African-American children have received in the school setting.

As socializing agents, schools are undeniably important to the Black community--not only because of what they can achieve, but also because they often can be quite destructive (Hall and Allen, 1983). Schools are the first institutions, for example, to apply the failure tag to many children in general and Black children in particular. Classification as being less than smart and always on the brink of failing is often the genesis of social malaise for African Americans.

This tag may start with the seeming innocence of an elementary school teacher breaking up a class into groups. But any semblance of innocence soon vanishes since all too frequently this process is actually a branding of some children as slow learners--too often an assessment based solely on their being African American (Smith, Simpson-Kirkland, Zimmern, Goldenstien & Pritchard, 1986). Students quickly pick up this message about who is ''smart'' and who is not (Bennett, 1979), so that the students themselves begin to inculcate these self-perceptions and attitudes.

Sure, the impact of the message is as powerful for the ''smart''

54

kids as it is for those deemed less than smart, but I am concerned mostly about the greater potential for damage among the latter-- who are too frequently African American and who may never be able to move beyond this initial classification.

Schools as Change Agents

Much of the literature which discusses organizational theory and change suggests that organizations rarely undergo meaningful change based on internal review. In fact, as Simon and March (1958) and Baron (1983), have shown, organizations resist change by relying on established standard operating procedures and ''satisfying'' alternatives to problems. External stimuli, therefore, are needed to prompt review, evaluation, and change. Schools and colleges are no different, and have provided their own evidence that substantive changes in policies, procedures, and practices result mainly from external stimuli. Prejudiced teachers who are resistant to changing those teaching behaviors not conducive to the growth and development of minority students, for instance, rarely alter their practices without external pressure (Bennett, 1979). The judicial system, as well as federal and state legislatures, have provided much of the external impetus for educational reforms toward equity in education during the sixties. Such external systems and the policies set forth by them remain important arbiters today.

The Jewish-American and Asian-American Communities: Models for Group Achievement

The mission of the public schools is to preserve and transmit the majority culture. They therefore will never by themselves become revolutionary agents of change. The only change that is likely to occur within the school context is change which does not potentially threaten the status quo or the majority group. Clearly, incremental change has not been successful in addressing the poor achievement, low self-esteem, and feelings of isolation and inferiority experienced by African-American students in the aggregate.

55

Once we recognize that schools will never embrace radical change, we can then explore another route: establishing settings outside of the schools for solutions to the historical patterns of Black children failing academically and socially.

Two ethnic settings serving as excellent examples are in the Jewish-American and in the more traditional Asian-American communities. They both have successfully created supplemental learning environments that run parallel to the mainstream school experience and nurture within children the necessary drive for academic achievement.

Examining these two communities and their practices will help us develop viable strategies for motivating and enhancing the academic performance and social adjustment of African-American children, who like traditional Jewish-American and Asian-American children, must compete and adjust as minorities.

One consistent and notable characteristic of both the traditional Jewish-American and Asian-American communities is that neither group has ever sought to have its cultural or historical tradition incorporated into the public educational process. Rather, both groups have viewed this task of cultural and historical instruction as a family and community responsibility, and therefore have provided their youngsters with an understanding of their cultural heritage in alternative learning settings and experiences *outside* the formal school setting.

Either explicitly or implicitly, both of these communities have recognized that the mainstream educational system will not provide their off-spring with positive cultural foundations. In essence, this understanding of cultural background and roots is vital to imparting children with a sense of their true identity and a perspective on who they are and what is possible for them to achieve. This approach inherently fosters both the conviction that education is a ticket to success and the belief that there is an "obligation to excel intellectually."

The message to be extrapolated here by African Americans is that family identification, support, and rewards for achievement provide children with a clear sense of direction and a mission for academic achievement.

What is the paramount function of Hebrew schools? It is to instruct Jewish youngsters about their cultural heritage, thereby helping them achieve a wholeness in their identity as Jewish-Americans. Another less apparent function served by this supplemental learning experience is providing a "leg up" in the mainstream classroom setting since it is apparent that a double dose of a structured learning environment will reinforce children's learning as well as their ability to learn.

More specifically, Hebrew schools place a premium on verbal abilities in terms of speech and composition. These values and skills are naturally brought back to the public classroom setting and enable many Jewish-American students to excel because of their well-developed communication skills.

The traditional Asian-American community likewise has provided stimulating external learning experiences for its children. One of my favorite stories, featured in the Atlanta Constitution (1985), showed how several families achieved financial success and some security after being in the United States approximately four years. This group of Korean families established a cultural school for their children and other Korean youngsters. The explicit goals of this school were two-fold: to help Korean children understand their position in a new society so that they would not be intimidated by the American cultural values and attitudes, and to help their children develop ethnic pride and identity based on their cultural lineage. Once again, the expectation for high academic achievement is reinforced by both the immediate family and the community at large.

Had the traditional Jewish-American and Asian-American communities left the responsibility of instructing their children about their cultural traditions to the public schools, the group pride and academic achievement that I am speaking about would be greatly diminished. By providing external learning environments, they have instilled in their children their values of family, community, and education. These historical connections strengthen the children's sense of identity and motivation to achieve in academic and professional settings. Equally important, the external support shields these minority children from the daunting norms of the majority culture. They are quite capable of overcoming institutionalized barriers to self-acceptance and social adjustment.

As I write this in the early nineties, the control of schooling in society remains in the hands of the dominant and powerful majority. The major curriculum and budget decisions, as well as the critical questions of who will be served and how, remain in the hands of the majority. Minority and poor parents, for the most part, remain uninvolved in the planning and execution of educational policies and programs.

Feelings of inadequacy and powerlessness experienced by African-American and other minority parents contribute to a pattern whereby they want to avoid the educational system. Schools continue to fail at managing this reality, preferring instead to blame the parents and thereby further alienating them from the educational process.

African-American parents are gravely concerned about the education received by their youngsters. However, when educational institutions convince these parents that no place exists for their concerns, the result is a set of parents who will not participate in the system. When schools recognize the importance of African-American parents in the educational process and provide non-anxiety producing opportunities for their involvement, the participation of these parents dramatically increases.

Public schools have insisted that all parental and community participation must take place in the formal school setting. Little if any outreach to the African-American community where the children and parents live has been attempted. If this historical trend of approach-avoidance is to be addressed, education officials must extend themselves, their efforts, and new community-based enterprises beyond the schoolyard's wall. Only when true outreach to the African-American and other non-majority communities is achieved will participation by these communities in the formal education process be improved.

You may have guessed by now that my own strategies designed to increase Black participation in school governance owe a great deal to my understanding of and appreciation for what the traditional

Jewish and traditional Asian communities in America have done. These strategies will focus on involving African-American parents, families, and communities in the education of African-American children within and without the mainstream education system. Without the development of such strategies, the unsettling pattern of maintaining the status quo and of pushing Black youngsters out of the educational arena will continue.

References

Baron, Robert. (1983). *Behavior in Organizations--Understanding and Managing the Human Side of Work*. Boston: Allyn and Bacon.

Bennett, C. (1979). Teacher prejudice as a mediating factor in student growth and development. *Viewpoints in Teaching and Learning*, 55 (2), 94-106.

Hall, M. & Allen, W. (1983). Race consciousness and achievement: Two issues in the study of Black graduate/professional students. *Integrated Education*, 56-61.

Knopf, I. J. (1979). *Childhood Psychopathology: A Developme Approach*. Englewood Cliffs: Prentice Hall.

Simon, H.A. & March, J.G. (1958). *Organizations*. New ' Wiley.

Smith, J, Simpson-Kirkland, D., Zimmern, J., Goldens' Prichard, K. (1986). The five most important prob' ing Black students today. *The Negro Educational* 61.

Wilson, Reginald, Carter, Deborah J. (1988). *M Education*, American Council on Educatio'

6

A Zebra Does Not Despise Its Own Stripes

Certain critical assumptions must be implanted in the mind set of the African-American community before it can develop a new philosophy of education that prepares its Black citizens as a group for educational success in America. The acceptance of this framework is essential if the blueprint I am proposing for the educational achievement of African Americans is to be successfully implemented.

Education as an Institution

One of the essential functions of public education is the preserving the majority culture, a function which on a philosophical level gnates the search for truth and which on a practical level minimizes status of socially disadvantaged minorities in the society. This preservation of the status quo, moreover, is a process which is in direct conflict with social theories advocating the value of institutional change. In particular, it contradicts classical Lewinian theory which states that change and constancy are relative concepts; that group life is never without change and that merely differences in amount and type of change exist (Lewin, 1947).

In order for African Americans and other socially disadvantaged minorities to secure a foothold in the educational process and, thereby, excel as a group, minorities must force a change. We must expand the function of education to reflect our hopes, dreams and aspirations. In particular, African Americans must assertively set forth a revised definition of education which preserves our historical and cultural knowledge as well as that of the majority. In the long run, this redirection will provide for a better quality of life for all.

Indeed--and as I think about the awe with which my own mother held the school system I was enrolled in I know this will sound blasphemous--African Americans must move beyond their traditional support for the institution. They will have to step back and become educational analysts and leaders who identify and assess barriers to achievement. Then they must set forth a plan for overcoming these barriers, utilizing the traditional strengths that are part of the community's resources.

They can no longer assume that the existing institution of education has their best interest in mind, given the fact that the elevation of any minority as a group will change the balance that typically keeps the majority in the top level positions of power and influence. Man's basic need for power (Maslow, 1970) suggests that it is ridiculous to think that any majority would institute voluntarily genuine efforts to alter the status quo significantly.

Inherent in the preservation of the majority culture is a second function performed by public schools--the transmission of the majority culture. America's non-majority groups have their cultural heritages, concerns, and idiosyncratic cultural differences supplanted ¹ a typically Waspish focus. This second function of educatio typically pursued subliminally. So we, "the dark and the differer often slow in recognizing this function and are therefore t developing and implementing counter measures.

For example, an African-American child may well not conceptualize that a lack of pictures in textbooks and on bulletin boards which portray Blacks in important roles perpetuates the concepts of majority intellectual and social superiority. This relative absence of contrasting role models, messages, and value systems was until recently never actively raised as an issue.

It is time for African Americans and other socially disadvantaged groups to examine these subliminal messages promulgated in the schools and to insist on integrating messages about their own histories, cultures and heroes. The ''dark and the different'' must take the initiative in restructuring the basis for deciding the educational messages and values which subconsciously as well as consciously shape the self-esteem and achievement of all children in the educational system.

Education of African Americans

We African Americans have been both unabashed proponents and luckless victims of the conversion syndrome, a condition which prompts us to believe wholeheartedly in the rhetoric and the promise of the American dream as well as the power of education to bring this dream to life. Despite the oppressive cultural, social, and legal barriers placed in front of Blacks during the periods of slavery, sharecropping, and urban ghetto life, the Black nation still believes totally in the rhetoric and promise found in the Constitution of the United States, the Bill of Rights, the Declaration of Independence, and the Emancipation Proclamation. Yet, in reality, upward mobility for Blacks in this promising society has been quite unidimensional. Black choices in life have been and remain largely limited. For us, education remains the most traveled direct route to upward mobility. And so as a rule, very few African Americans look forward to inherited wealth, power, or position. Despite the fact that education in America is rooted in a pervasively elitist tradition, this belief in education's importance permeates the Black community regardless of socioeconomic standing.

We know that colonists who came to the New World were not, for the most part, the elite of Western European society. Yet they carried with them the medieval notion that education is an elitist prerogative reserved for the children of the nobility and the clergy, and they set up educational institutions to reflect this notion. Serfs (the poor and disenfranchised) had not been educated in medieval Europe. So the charter of America's first institution of higher education set up by clergyman John Harvard in 1636 declares its purpose to be the provision of education for the children of ministers and for property owners. Property owners at this point in history translates into white men only.

Other educational institutions that were established after the founding of Harvard mirrored the same or similar elitist assumptions found in the Harvard Charter. My point is that American educational institutions, both lower and higher, were imbued from their founding with certain pervasive elitist underpinnings that have made achievement by groups outside this narrowly defined mainstream to be difficult at best and impossible at worst.

Those minority groups that have been excluded and punished for their ascribed physical, behavioral, and verbal characteristics include African Americans, Native Americans, Mexican Americans, and women (Gay, 1974; Robinson, Robinson & Bickel, 1980). The failure of individuals from these groups to achieve, in the aggregate, in the American public education system can certainly be better understood when the history of education in this country is examined.

Only then can it be clear that education as an institution and process in America has steadfastly failed to incorporate values, attitudes, or interests from minority groups. And this refusal has created structural, emotional and psychological barriers for members of these groups generally and for African Americans particularly-- barriers which have made achievement and success in the school setting very difficult. The American school system was never designed to educate Black youngsters and accordingly these youngsters have largely failed in the American school system. *We have never been zebras of the same stripe.* Tragically, their failure has reinforced the continuing myth of intellectual inferiority (Bennett, 1979).

If American society is to prepare its workforce of the twenty-first century to compete in a global economy, fundamental changes in public schools and in American communities must be encouraged. For their part, schools must act to extend to African Americans and other minorities what historically they have done so well with upper and middle-class White males--assist them in personifying the principles espoused by the founders of America.

The African-American Community's Response

With this background, the African-American community must decide what public schools can do for our children and what must be accomplished from within the citizenry to promote high academic achievement and the subsequent entrance into a diverse and changing job market.

The idea of life chances, introduced by Max Weber, seems to me to be most relevant when considering these challenges (Gerth & Wright, 1972). When reexamined in terms of the Black community, this concept provides helpful insights and directions for further action in the struggle for educational opportunity and equity.

Weber uses the term to describe the degree of access to economic and political power that a group has in a given society. Unquestionably, African Americans continue to have less access to economic and real political power and influence than their majority counterparts. Weber suggests that when a subset of a society does not enjoy equal access, this oppressed group develops certain "lifestyles." These lifestyles allow individuals to cope with and ward off the collective disappointment, pain, and rejection dealt to them by mainstream society (Tribble, 1970).

Many of the practices and behaviors of African Americans reflect Weber's concept of lifestyle adaptation. Talking loudly, "being cool," and behaving aggressively are a few examples of practices often assumed by poor Black youth because these conventions are antithetical to the primary values of society and its schools. In my mind, these youngsters participate in such practices as one way of responding to institutional racism, labels of failure, and overwhelm-

64

ing feelings of powerlessness and hopelessness which are so prevalent in American schools and their indigenous communities. The kids who were acting up in the classroom down the hall from me in Vineland's H.L. Reber Junior High were behaving that way because they were trying to cope with the enfeebling experiences of poverty.

My blueprint, therefore, is predicated on the assumption that in order to achieve group educational success and alter the life chances of our children, we must change the very lifestyle that these children emulate. This lifestyle must be modified by setting up a standard of group educational excellence; it must become "hip" and "cool" to achieve educationally. To be successful, this new standard must be defined and nurtured by the collective community which provides the necessary inner strength that Black children need so that they will, in the words of Dr. Bernard C. Watson, "Succeed In Spite Of The System" (Watson, 1974).

References

Bennett, C. (1979). Teacher prejudice as a mediating factor in student growth and development. *Viewpoints in Teaching and Learning.* 55 (2), 94-106.

Brophy, J. E. & Good, T. L. (1974). *Teacher-Student Relationships: Causes and Consequences.* New York: Holt, Rinehart and Winston, 196-197.

Clark, R. (1983). *Family Life and School Achievement: Why Poor Black Children Succeed or Fail.* Chicago: The University of Chicago Press.

Drury, D. (1980). Black self-esteem and desegregated schools. *Sociology of Education,* 53, 88-103.

Gay, G. (1974). Differential dyadic interactions of Black and white teachers with Black and white pupils in recently desegregated social studies classrooms: A function of teacher and pupil ethnicity. National Institute of Education, Washington, D.C.

Gerth, H. & Mills, C. W. (1972). *From Weber; Essays in Sociology.* New York: Oxford University Press.

Green, R.L., & Brydon, J. (1975). Investing in youth: An approach to discipline in urban schools. *Discipline and Learning.* Washington, D.C.: National Education Association.

Lewin, K. (1947). Group decision and social change. In T.M. Newcomb & E.L. Hartley (Eds.) *Readings in Social Psychology.* New York: Holt, Rinehart and Winston.

Maslow, A.H. (1970). *Motivation and Personality (2nd Ed.).* New York: Harper and Row.

Robinson, S., Robinson, A. & Bickel, F. (1980). Desegregation: A bibliographic review of teacher attitudes and Black students. *The Negro Educational Review.* 31 (2), 48-59.

Simmons, R., Brown, L., Bush, D. & Blyth, D. (1978). Self-esteem and achievement of Black and white adolescents. *Social Problems.* 26, 86-96.

Tribble, Israel, (1970). Motivational counseling: a Black educational imperative. *Educational Leadership.* Association for Supervision Training and Curriculum Development, Volume 28, No. 3, 12/70.

Watson, Bernard C. (1974) *In Spite of the System.* Cambridge: Ballinger Publishing.

Woodward, W.D. & Salzer, R. T. (1971). Black children's speech and teachers' evaluations. *Urban Education*. July-October, 167-173.

7

Those Who Are Absent Are Always Wrong

T he African-American community's active participation is critical
to the success of this blueprint since its cornerstone belief is that our
children must receive supplemental education--steeped in African-
American values and traditions and absolutely essential to developing
and maintaining what I call a group achievement culture among our
youth. Nurtured systematically under this culture, our youngsters will
be motivated to view educational achievement as a positive experience that requires learning beyond the classroom. But to manage this
challenge successfully, the African-American community must establish new modes of behavior and practice. It cannot build a house
for last year's summer. Again, we'll have to look carefully at how we
have responded in the past to our predicament, and then revise
thoroughly those tactics.

Before looking at that history though, it is important to recognize that the Black citizenry in America possesses a historically unprecedented abundance of human, physical, and financial resources. These resources--plentiful in quality as well as in quantity--can help provide the context for setting up a new Black philosophy of education that places great value on achievement.

But these resources will be useless without a change in thinking. You cannot build a house for last year's summer. And the basic change must be from that of our historical posture of reaction to one of dynamic, assertive participation.

To be sure, this posture, given the socio-historical underpinnings of the Black experience in America, had some validity. The nature of the oppression experienced by African Americans from the plantation throughout the sharecropping system defined and reinforced this reactive course. And it continued to be bolstered during the Great Migration of 1915, which led to the establishment of urban ghettoes so prevalent in today's Northeastern, Mid-western and Western cities.

We have been in an almost constant posture of reacting to our state of powerlessness and dependency--the residual historical circumstances which have defined the life chances for the vast majority of African Americans. At the same time, negative societal attitudes, perceptions, and denigrating practices which made economic and social mobility extremely difficult, if not impossible, were the central features of this impotency.

Although opportunities have increased to some degree for many in the African-American population, there remains still an omnipresent struggle within our citizenry to overcome the reactive posture in which we find ourselves. One approach that makes sense to me--if we are to meet today's challenges--require us firstly to expose the nature of past and present oppression and discriminatory attitudes and practices that have been a pervasive stitch in the American institutional fabric. Secondly, we must then develop our own programs that will counter this negative historical view of Blacks as a dependent and powerless group.

In other words, before a culture of achievement can be attained, we must understand fully what the impact of oppression has been on this community and how the community has persevered nevertheless. A central part of this review of our history is the evidence that, despite the obstacles, there are countless individual examples of African Americans who have excelled.

It is also important to note again--if we are to redirect the African-American's community's approach to be dynamically assertive--is that two of the essential functions of education are first the preservation and then the transmission of the majority culture. Consequently, the primary charge of the schools is the preservation of the majority status quo and its political, social and economic power. Black history and culture beyond entertainment have no relevance for the majority and therefore are excluded, by design, from the core curriculum of the public schools or in most post-secondary institutions.

When these premises about the function of schools are identified as basic values and control mechanisms that permeate the educational and other societal structures, then one quickly gains insight into how affluence, power and education attainment are linked.

There is a direct correlation between affluence, power and success on the one side, and educational attainment on the other. Similarly, the converse is true about poverty and educational failure. These correlations indicate that those who enjoy the advantage of having their culture, history, values, attitudes, and hope for a better future transmitted and preserved on a systematic basis--these persons perform well academically. Those who are not a part of the majority culture and don't have their needs fulfilled by the total school setting do not perform as well.

Alexander Solzhenitsyn, the renowned Soviet ex-patriot author, in the *Gulag Archipelago* writes, ''If you dwell on the past, you lose one eye; if you forget the past, you lose both eyes'' (Harper & Row, New York 1974-78). An assertive stance for the Black community is one which will keep an eye on the past, remembering still that success in the future will be predicated both on the ability to understand the past and the ability to develop strategies for future success. If we can change our thinking accordingly, then I believe we can attain the culture of achievement, and that this new way of assessing educational achievement will increase the numbers of Black citizens who will be competitive by any set of standards. They will then progress individually and collectively in the economic, social and political arenas.

In Search of Excellence

Before developing my own blueprint, I wanted to examine other successful models. I thought that I could find some direction and insight for my own efforts and further ensure that my path would have the best chance for success. In approaching the complex and extraordinary task of developing a group achievement culture within the Black community, I discovered a model in the thoughts and concepts developed by Peters and Waterman in their book *In Search of Excellence* (1982).

These authors examined the best corporations in America and identified what features, values, and characteristics created and maintained their success in the marketplace. Peters and Waterman did not discover new techniques of management; quite to the contrary, the authors simply reaffirmed the importance of basic human relations. Individuals increase their productivity when they feel respected; respect is communicated by managers through active listening, through responsiveness to the needs of their clients and employees, and through rewarding of creativity rather than stifling it with bureaucratic detail.

I maintain that the framework used by *In Search of Excellence* can, with some modification, be applied to the African-American community and its need to develop a culture of group achievement for young people. Following their approach, it seemed to me that the key to our dilemma would be to identify the cultural groups who are most successful in the American education system. Studying these groups, I thought, would provide insights into the practices, behaviors, and values which must be then inculcated in Black youth and institutionalized within the community so that educational achievement will emerge as a desired and expected outcome.

As I said earlier, two groups were identified as having performed well and consistently so in American schools--traditional Jewish-American and Asian-American students. Consequently I used their experiences to help me develop the group achievement culture model for Blacks. After my analysis, I discovered that there are several attributes which can be duplicated by my model for enhancing group achievement.

Here are the principal attributes:

1) Providing supplemental learning experiences in the home and in culturally oriented part-time schools in the community
2) Involving parents in learning activities and support roles at home and school
3) Furnishing community role models for the children
4) Stimulating learning through books, magazines, and newspapers that are read by parents and significant others
5) Providing opportunities for public speaking and for displaying talents and competencies in the community
6) Communicating to children (via parents and the community) that they are expected to achieve
7) Reinforcing of academic effort and success by the family and community.

These behaviors and practices have furthermore been validated in educational research as significant factors in academic achievement (Good & Brophy, 1973; Clark, 1983). That is, causal relationships do exist between parental interest, supplemental learning experiences, and positive reinforcement for achievement and academic performance. So, the challenge of the blueprint is to translate these identified behaviors and practices into a model that can be implemented in every African-American neighborhood.

The African-American Community

The initial step in establishing a model for group achievement culture in the African-American community, which as we know possesses a large store of human and to a lesser degree financial resources never before in such abundance, is to identify a location conveniently accessible to many youngsters at which their public education may be augmented with a uniquely Black socio-cultural orientation.

Without question, the church is the most readily identifiable location for a number of reasons. It often is the only institution in the African-American neighborhood that is financially, socially and politically controlled by Black people. Furthermore, it is the epicenter of social and political activity for nearly every Black community, typically has the best facilities in that community and usually is available for community activities at least five days per week. Certainly, the church has the tradition and credibility in the community to help lead at this critical juncture.

In each African-American community, regardless of size or location, there is at least one or more significant churches that could assist in establishing the group achievement culture. Nurturing youth and assisting in the cultural and economic development of the community must not be viewed by the church or the community at large as being in direct competition or opposition to saving souls. Rather, the church and community must begin to see saving minds and souls as a positive and healthful symbiotic relationship which has the potential of ensuring the future development of the community.

No longer is it sufficient for the African-American citizenry to just believe in "the system." By contrast, they must continue to participate in the mainstream and *also* create their own internal support systems which enable and ensure the success of African-American children within the mainstream.

It is critical that Black churches assume a leadership role and an assertive stance in this drive for group achievement. A wonderful lesson about church power can be learned from Southern majority churches during the period of public school desegregation following the 1954 Supreme Court decision of *Brown versus the Board of Education*. While Black church leaders were urging their communities to enroll in the public schools in the early sixties, white churches on the other hand were busy raising funds to build school annexes to their churches. Of course, these annexes served as no more than an alternative to the newly desegregated schools. In fact, it is my view that the development of the current television ministry and the evangelical/fundamentalist movement as an economic and political tool grew out of the rise in these broadly based "new" parochial

schools. Equally noteworthy is that the establishment of these parochial schools may be identified as the beginning of what today is the
very well-organized politically and economically powerful religious
right.

It is now time to maximize the emotional, physical, and psychic
resources that the church can offer our communities. Like their white
counterparts of the late fifties and early sixties, it is critical that Black
clergy identify the resources they can offer as positive and constructive alternatives or supplements to the educational process. By
contributing their leadership to help establish the culture of group
achievement, the Black church can truly ensure future progress.

Where should it start? The African-American church can intro-
duce the group achievement model in the Sunday school, which
remains the introductory core of the church experience for many
youth. For example, by requiring these children to write a simple
paragraph each Sunday on that day's Bible lesson, churches could
begin to contribute to the group achievement culture. Sunday school
teachers and other capable adults in the church could critique, correct,
and explain the corrections on each of the assignments. It is highly
likely and strongly argued that the children's achievement would
improve individually and collectively as a function of this supplemental learning experience offered in a supportive setting.

Additionally, other positive residuals would take place. African-
American adults would have a specific avenue by which they could
contribute to the growth and nurturing of their children; participation
by these adults and the children in other church activities would also
occur. Certainly, this is but one example of how the church, by
opening its doors and coordinating volunteers from the church and the
community-at-large, can begin the intervention process which will
move the community toward the group achievement culture that will
make it "cool" for Black youth to achieve academically.

When asked to identify what made the difference in their personal
and professional development, successful African Americans invari-
ably identify a significant adult. This significant role model is not
always Black and certainly not always a teacher. But the significant
adult is an individual who has achieved some measure of success, who

has stability, and who has cared enough to touch and influence a youngster's life. For me, it was Mr. Krouse, who pushed me toward making a mark. These life-enhancing interactions can be formally cultivated in the Black church. That is, the church has the opportunity to create a setting which encourages and formalizes youth-adult interactions while sponsoring and extending structured Black voluntaryism. Each community has the wherewithal to mobilize their human, physical, and spiritual resources. The mobilization will result in the development, strengthening, and institutionalization of the culture of group achievement. It is through such volunteer commitments that a bond between neighbors, between generations, and between existing interests in the African-American community is generated.

I have said that the African-American populace has failed to take sufficient advantage of the public and private resources available to it because it lacks a vision and a plan. Without a viable plan, resources available and eventually allocated have been fragmented in their use and certainly in their effectiveness. Knowing that success often breeds success, it seems clear to me the community must show its willingness, ability, and success at funding and operating programs directed at nurturing its own youth in order to obtain external resources. Once Black-controlled organizations like churches, fraternities, sororities and other civic groups have created track records as successful intervention and change agents, external resources will become more readily available from both the Black and majority community. But the first task at hand is for leaders to commit to the vision and the blueprint and initiate programs in the churches and elsewhere in the community to begin the critical process of providing supplemental learning in a nurturing, stable environment for this young population so critical to the nation's future.

References

Clark, R. (1983). *Family Life and School Achievement: Why Poor Black Children Succeed or Fail.* Chicago: The University of Chicago Press.

Good, T. and Broph, J. (1973). *Looking in Classrooms.* New York: Harper & Row.

Peters, T. and Waterman, R. II. (1982). *In Search of Excellence: Lessons From America's Best Run Companies.* New York: Warner Books.

Solzhenitsyn, Alexander, (1974). *Gulag Archipelago.* New York: Harper & Row.

8

We Start as Fools and Become Wise Through Experience

As citizens and taxpayers, the African-American populace has a proprietary interest in what happens to the public schools. Accordingly, the public school system must not be treated with benign neglect; rather, positive alternatives must be developed and implemented which will alter the institutional framework of public education. The change that I anticipate will be from the current system which implicitly (and sometimes explicitly) condones racist practices and promotes perennial academic failure of African-American youngsters--to an educational climate where all children have true opportunities for personal development and success.

The change envisioned in my blueprint includes empowering students and developing community-based supplemental learning programs. Further, I expect that the model will lead not only to improvements in student achievement but also to changes in the public schools. And altering the system is critical since ninety-eight percent of African-American children will receive their education in public settings.

Part of the reason for such high percentages is that frankly, in the vast majority of African-American families, financial resources do not exist to send children to private schools. Further, the historically conservative nature of the Black polity often prohibits our considering private schools as viable educational alternatives. This hesitation to invest or participate substantially in private schooling persists in spite of the knowledge that the public schools are failing to prepare adequately African-American youngsters for full social, economic, and political participation.

There is certainly enough evidence about the successes that non-public educational environments have had with Black youngsters. James Coleman and his colleagues' research (1982) suggests that parochial schools, notably Catholic academies, have been very effective with our African-American youth. Accordingly, the success of parochial schools offers the kind of model that *In Search of Excellence* encourages us to use to obtain direction and insights into how the Black community may improve the educational achievement of our youngsters.

Clearly, public education will not be the site of revolutionary or radical change. They are, as I have said, understandably invested in maintaining the status quo, and have made changes that have been only incremental at best. Many governmental programs like Head Start, Follow-Through and Upward Bound have had notable results, but even these provide opportunities for only a very small segment of the youth population.

We must face the fact: the time has come for educational programs to reach beyond the missionary sphere and develop replicable models for change which suggest alternatives that can be introduced and merged into the larger educational structure.

There are some models which, if integrated into the larger educational structure, can deal constructively with the problem. Specifically, I shall discuss the five models which I have designed to address many of the conflicts which exist within public educational institutions and programs as they relate to African-American children in particular and all children in general. These models should be considered by community organizations as a collection of alternative strategies which may be used in combination or singularly to address problems and issues in the public education system.

1. The Cooperative Model

The Cooperative Planning Model provides for more effective use of resources--financial, physical, and human--in educational programs. Many of the programs funded by the federal and/or state governments are designed to provide enriching educational experiences for African Americans and other socially disadvantaged and low-income persons. Often, however, the services these programs render are parallels of already existing approaches. For example, programs like Head Start are still run separately and apart from the mainstream early childhood program. What would happen if these programs overlapped? My guess is that services, facilities, funds and personnel could be utilized much more efficiently than is currently the case.

By developing collaborative and cooperative relationships between various agencies and institutions, schools can streamline programs and thereby not only save dollars, but also have an impact on the institutions involved by cultivating mutual goals and interests.

Streamlining may include using the community as a learning laboratory, consequently supporting the blueprint for a group achievement culture in the African-American community. Since public education can no longer afford to remain isolated from the larger community, a cooperative spirit needs to be developed not only between formal education groups, but also between these interests and the community at large.

As an illustration, concerned adults from the community can help assume some counseling responsibilities in the schools. These counselor surrogates can be found in the churches, among parents, and other professionals. They can be valuable to the schools for several reasons: (1) they can help ensure that all students regardless of color or gender receive counseling; (2) they can begin to alter the school's image from being what is now a custodial screening agent committed to maintaining the status quo, to being an institution which enables young people to know and pursue viable goals while attempting to reach their maximum potential, and (3) they can serve as symbols for African-American and other minority children that their adult communities really do care and actively do support their educational pursuits.

2. The Staff Training Model

The Staff Training Model is designed to improve the serviceableness of the organization by enhancing the effectiveness of school personnel on a systematic basis. Not until it is optimally productive can a public school possibly be responsive to the ever-changing needs of its students--especially the African-American population--and thereby maximize these students' academic success. It seems almost ludicrous to me that, compared to corporations, school systems at the lower level spend so little of their budget on staff development.

The model features basic components of training and evaluation, and at the same time it is flexible enough for adaptation at various levels of the school system.

I have relied on the theories and concepts of staff and organizational development of such theorists as Douglas McGregor (1967), Frederick Herzberg (1976), Chris Argyris (1976), Rensis Likert (1967) and Abraham Maslow (1965). Their work suggests the following:

1. Supervisors should trust subordinates to be more responsible about their individual job performances;
2. Supervisors should permit subordinates to participate in job development;
3. Supervisors should replace much of the mechanic structure, characteristic of most institutions, with a more humane approach to organization.

Of utmost importance is the transmission of values, both directly and indirectly, to students in the educational programs, and especially in the training component. The following values, therefore, will be at the heart of the staff development process:

1. Continuing growth in effectiveness of individuals and the organization;
2. Open and direct communication within and across organizational boundaries;
3. Mutual support and trust among team members;
4. Avoidance of depersonalization, and
5. Reinforcement for and acceptance of individual responsibility

Further, there is a set of explicit, bedrock beliefs which should surround the educational setting:

1. Educators should trust their students to be more responsible and more active learners;
2. Educators should permit students to participate in the definition of their own learning, and
3. Educators should replace much of the mechanical structure characteristic of most institutions with a more humane and student-oriented approach.

Meanwhile, three basic phases of the staff development process are emphasized: pre-service, in-service, and post-service.

Pre-service focuses on the recruitment/selection process since the quality of individuals hired for a program determines, to a large extent, the type and amount of training needed. Therefore, staff should be selected who demonstrate competence in interpersonal and group behavior techniques as well as solid dedication to program objectives.

If enough careful attention is given to the pre-service training of new staff members, then the amount of time needed for follow-up training will be reduced. Accordingly, this training must emphasize the concept of accountability, where the end results are of primary importance and where staff members are assisted in developing their own performance objectives. In addition, techniques like team building, intergroup dynamics, role playing and simulation games should be used in this pre-service phase. Finally, video-taping of these exercises will enable participants to observe behaviors and skill levels in specific situations.

Simultaneously, the in-service training phase will contain two distinct training modules: one devoted to personal growth and the other devoted to organizational growth.

On the personal level, strengths and weaknesses of staff are explored and a plan is developed to improve deficiencies. On the organizational level, the staff learns how to make improvements--yet building and maintaining key organizational links--by using the valuable technique of feedback. It is precisely this combination of carefully planned personal and organizational learning experiences of the in-service phase that strengthens the staff development process, and consequently, the overall educational program.

Finally, the post-service training phase of the staff development process provides the opportunity for a critical review of the results of individual training components. Overall effectiveness can be determined in the usual manner--by determining how well the performance objectives were achieved.

In conclusion, the staff development process, which should be a dynamic, continual process, is adaptable to a variety of educational requirements. But in the three phases, training directed toward organizational growth, collecting data, diagnosing program needs and designing and implementing action programs are keys to the entire effort. Of course too, evaluation, feedback, and training modifications must be taking place continually. And finally I must emphasize the importance of accountability and the measurement of accountability by how well objectives are reached.

3. The Core Group Model

The Core Group Model is a motivational process designed to serve as a bridge between the expectations and goals of African-American and other socially disadvantaged minority and low-income students on the one hand, and the expectations of the educational institutions who are charged with serving these students on the other. By motivation, I mean that process by which incentives toward positive action are offered. A core group is a small circle of students who meet on a regular basis with a carefully selected leader and a trained assistant.

The Core Group Model is based on assumptions that are supported by research on self-concept and low aspiration levels. For example, James Coleman's study (1990) indicates that no significant difference exists between the expressed self-concepts of African-American and majority students; in fact these students have higher aspirations than their majority counterparts who share the same socio-economic status. Coleman's study, when combined with the experience of federal programs which were flooded with minority applicants, certainly suggests to me that goal attainment is *not* necessarily related to low self-concept or low levels of aspiration. Logically, then the question that remains, is what prevents these students from achieving their aspirations?

The answer is conflict--opposing interests and principles--which arises from the differences between the expectations and goals of the students versus those of the educational institutions. Moreover, there is an additional gap between the students' aspirations and their abilities to translate these aspirations into action.

These types of conflict cause the frustrations which students so often feel and which often blunt their ability to succeed academically and socially; these types of conflicts may well contribute to students dropping out of school. To be sure, some conflict is inherent in the educational setting: schools as organizations may have goals and agendas which are not always in consort with student goals and agendas. But the lessening and resolving of these conflicts gripping African-American and other minority students would result in improvement of these students' abilities to have their aspirations actualized. (Cobbs and Grier, 1968)

The Core Group Model is the very process through which conflicts are reduced or resolved by creating an environment that is conducive to the free articulation of feelings and aspirations. Once they are better aware and understand the sources of conflict and moreover have a forum for expressing these feelings, students can begin to cope with conflict. The model suggests restructuring the academic setting so that expressions of conflict, aspirations, and goals can take place normally.

Equally importantly, the model emphasizes developing a plan by which these aspirations can be realized. Of course this planning necessitates a realistic assessment of skills and goals. For example, if a student expresses the desire to become an engineer but has none of the skills necessary for that field, several options can be explored. The first option is to plan for the student to get the necessary skills by taking courses and receiving academic enrichment. A second option is to explore other fields, with different requirements but which may meet the student's career goal. So the model focuses not only on achieving goals, but also on determining if the goals are realistic and attainable (Tribble, 1972).

Since the environment that the staff creates for the core group is the foundation for the effectiveness of those students, the selection of personnel in the Core Group Model is absolutely critical. Although traditional credentials are of little importance in the selection of core group leaders, they must consist of individuals who are willing and able to establish open and trusting relationships (Tribble, 1970). The core group leader is to act as a scientific observer whose contact with the students is very personal but not dominating. In fact, the leader is not to have direct influence over the students at all; rather, the greatest value is derived from the leader's interaction with students.

Further, a core group leader must be supportive and possess sensitivity, warmth, good listening skills, a positive approach to life and objectivity in the group process. And too a leader must possess psychological insight and be able to respond to difficult situations which may arise. Receptivity to feedback is a must. Similar criteria should be used when selecting assistants to work with the leader.

Structurally, a core group includes ten to fifteen students taken from a cross-section of the student population; a leader, and an assistant. Ideally, the core groups are scheduled to meet both before and after classes. The meetings before classes are designed to develop the students' awareness and understanding of themselves and the conflicts that they and others may experience. The clarification of personal expectations and goals are encouraged by the leader and assistant; mechanisms to encourage students to express themselves include general discussion, games, role-playing, and video-taping.

The closing sessions, held after classes, continue the activities from the first session. Emphasis in these sessions is on making an "attitude check": to see how each student feels about the experiences of the day and if any conflicts have arisen.

Journals as well as audio-tapes and video-tapes can be used to help students learn how to learn about themselves. Creativity in expression and support for personal communication is essential for the core group model to be maximally successful, so leaders are encouraged to integrate new communication technologies as they become available.

To reiterate, the Core Group Model is designed to help students adjust to the education environment. By resolving or reducing certain conflicts that minority and low-income students confront, school personnel can, I suggest, improve both the motivation level of students and the likelihood that the students can achieve their goals.

4. The Flexible Curriculum Model

The Flexible Curriculum Model is designed to ensure maximum involvement of students in the learning process. The assumption of the model is that students can better internalize concepts and theories of learning which have been made relevant to them. A flexible curriculum is one in which the fundamental principles and concepts of a subject area are condensed into a package representing roughly twenty percent of the total discipline. The remaining eighty percent of the subject area is constructed and further developed by direct student participation with the teacher acting as a facilitator and guide. Therefore, the content of each discipline is reduced to its lowest common denominator--the basic principles, ideas, and concepts of the discipline--which, in turn must be translated into practical terms using experiences shared by students.

To illustrate, the concept of family expressed in sociological, cultural and historical terms could then be expanded upon by the class who would define the different kinds of families in the group--that is, nuclear, single parent, guardian, older sibling and the like.

The curriculum is the heart of the educational process but it has been allowed to stagnate and become so entrenched that it fails to provide a learning process meaningful to most students, especially minority students. This new curriculum model, explicitly designed for student participation, is developed around a plan which combines the academic experience with practical application at all levels of the learning process.

The teacher of any course to be offered in this model must have sufficient time to analyze critically the materials of the curriculum. The teacher selects the basic ideas, principles and concepts which are essential to the course, then presents them to the students in an initial meeting; the students then select a number of the basic ideas, principles and concepts on which to focus. This last step provides a viable means for students to determine course direction.

Once the major areas of concentration are decided, the time allotted for instruction is divided into two parts. The first part of the course emphasizes the instructor's role in familiarizing the students with the major areas of concentration within the discipline so that each student can demonstrate his or her understanding of the discipline by applying those ideas, principles and concepts. The second part emphasizes the student's role and responsibility for active learning. The teacher, at this point, acts as a facilitator and guide rather than a conventional dispenser of knowledge.

What is central here is augmented student involvement through peer presentations. Students learn from one another; student participation in the learning and teaching process increases both self-confidence and academic performance.

By facilitating the learning process, actively involving the student in that process, and reinforcing that learning through practical applications, the Flexible Curriculum Model prepares students for active participation in society.

5. The Conflict Resolution Model

A natural state of conflict exists in the public education system, and I am thoroughly convinced that it prevents positive learning from occurring.

The Conflict Resolution Model uses confirmation, the most effective though least practical form of resolving dissension, to quell the conflicts that arise in institutional settings. A certain amount of conflict is inevitable in any organization since the needs of the individual and the needs of the organization can never be wholly compatible. Educational institutions, oddly enough, because of the goals and principles espoused, have a lower level of conflict than other types of organizations. But the friction exists.

Because of the historical background and psychosocial makeup of most African-American children, they arrive at the public school setting already at odds, already clashing with school expectations. This strife is not to be confused with lack of readiness for learning or age-stage developmental unreadiness. On the contrary, as I have maintained consistently, research shows that the public school system is skewed favorably toward the mainstream, imbued with Eurocentric, middle-class values which do not mesh well with the Afrocentric mind set. African-American and other historically disadvantaged children fall generally into the low-income category and are usually bi-cultural and/or bi-lingual. This combination of distinctions produces immediate dissonance and alienation for the student. And so the issue at the base of the conflict is really one of race and class. An increase in this level of conflict in an educational institution is usually a superficial manifestation of a more serious and deep-rooted situation. All too often, efforts to resolve this heightened conflict are directed toward the surface condition or the symptoms of the real problem.

But the real problem must be addressed, and that means that all sides in a conflict are brought together in good faith. Then, the time allotted for the resolution of the conflict is unlimited; the factions represented in the dialogue must have all the time necessary to identify the causes of the friction. This time factor may mean the total disruption of a normal organizational pattern, but conflict resolution is a learning experience and therefore is as valuable or more valuable than the usual pattern.

Another step in the conflict resolution process is the utilization of an outside moderator who is both objective and humanistically oriented. This moderator has a delicate role. He or she must be a skilled group leader who is familiar with the problems involved; he or she must serve as a facilitator who can raise questions, suggest procedures, and generally facilitate the operations of the total group. As an ''outsider'' the moderator is never part of the true power structure, and consequently is not actively involved in the conflict and cannot be identified with any particular faction.

The moderator should help develop and maintain the trust relationship between vying factions. This relationship is essential and develops only if each faction feels that its participation is valued and has an impact. Also, each faction must care about the conflict and, equally importantly, want to resolve this conflict.

The initial arguments used by each side to present its case can act as a catharsis. Further, group development directs the cluster from venting its emotions. Instead, focus will be on constructive actions based on mutual trust. Some factions will arrive at this essential trust factor before others; however, to achieve true resolution, all factions must ultimately place some trust in the process and in one another.

I have tried to present five models that can serve as a framework for developing school and community-based programs. All of the models are based upon humanistic values: respect for all individuals, the desirability of collective and cooperative behavior patterns, and faith in the individual's ability to assume responsibility for his or her actions. These models can serve as exciting baselines by which individual schools, systems, or communities can work to improve the public educational process for minority student needs. These models, especially when coupled with supplemental community-based education programs, will bolster the opportunities for African-American and socially disadvantaged minority students to be more competitive and eventually become active, productive members of society.

References

Argyris, C. (1976). *Increasing Leadership Effectiveness.*
New York: Wiley.

Cobbs, P. & Grier, W. (1968). *Black Rage.* New York: Basic Books.

Coleman, J. (1990). *Equality and Achievement in Education.*
Boulder: West View Press.

Coleman, J., Noffer, T., & Kilgore, S. (1982). *High School
Achievement: Public, Catholic, and Private Schools Compared.*
New York: Basic Books.

Herzberg, F. (1976). *The Managerial Choice to Be Efficient and to
Be Human.* Homewood, IL: Dow Jones-Irwin.

Likert, R. (1967). *The Human Organization; Its Management and
Value.* New York: McGraw-Hill.

Maslow, A. (1965). *Eupsychian Management; A Journal by Abraham
H. Maslow.* Homewood, IL.: Dow Jones-Irwin.

McGregor, D. & Dennis, W. G. (eds). (1967). *The Professional
Manager.* New York: McGraw-Hill.

Pruitt, D. & Rubin, J. (1986). *Social Conflict.* New York: Random
House.

Tribble, Jr., I. (1972) *Study Report Special Summer Session.* Mills
College, Oakland, California.

Tribble, Jr., I. (1972) *The Core Group Model: A Motivational
Process for Reducing Conflict in Education for Black Students.*
California State University, Hayward, California.

Tribble, Jr., I. (1970). Motivational counseling: a Black educational imperative. *Education Leadership.* Association for Supervision Training and Curriculum Development, 28 (3).

9

No Matter How Long the Night, the Day Is Sure To Come

I t is one thing to have conceptually sound and well-researched ideas about improving educational achievement. It is entirely another to have the resources necessary to make those ideas come alive and grow into an actual program. In the case of my own good fortune, the resources in fact were made possible in the state of Florida through a 1984 grant from the McKnight Foundation located in Minneapolis, Minnesota.

My involvement with the foundation was quite unexpected, since I was quite happy coordinating master planning for the state university system of Florida through its Board of Regents. After many discussions about the new program however, I sensed that a tremendous opportunity was available, so I accepted the offer to serve as the first executive director of the McKnight Programs in Higher Education in Florida.

In the previous chapters, I've presented the historical and philosophical framework which gave rise to many of the principles and programmatic ideas undergirding the McKnight effort, which I directed. This framework synthesizes and directly reflects my thinking gained through more than thirty years of experience in education. From this background emerges several basic assumptions about the African-American community and its stance toward education:

1. African-American children, along with other socially disadvantaged children, come into this world intellectually endowed to be educationally successful barring brain damage or some other debilitating social, psychological or physical infirmity.

2. The African-American community cares deeply about education and possesses an abiding commitment to the process and the institution. The community understands fundamentally that the progress of individuals and the collective community depends almost unilaterally on educational achievement.

3. The African-American community has demonstrated the ultimate in ''religious faith'' about schools and expects them to do the best possible for their children.

These three assumptions are essential to educational success. To restate, schools and teachers must believe that African-American children can learn. They must also understand that the community from which these children are produced is their historical ally and that support for education runs deep in the fabric of the community. And, finally, the strong faith exhibited by the African-American community can be harnessed to assist the schools in being more successful at providing a positive and productive educational experience for each child.

Within this context, the McKnight Programs in Higher Education were launched. Because of restraints we had on our finances and time, it was necessary to move with dispatch; so we devised a model steeped in community and organizational program development rather than focusing on research and evaluation. Here is a historical sketch of the McKnight Programs, its components, phases and accomplishments to date.

Historical Sketch

The McKnight Foundation was established in 1953 by William L. McKnight and Maude L. McKnight to support goals that encourage and promote charitable, scientific, literary and educational efforts. It is toward the goal of promoting educational initiatives that the Florida Endowment Fund for Higher Education was established in 1987. Its predecessor is the McKnight Program in Higher Education founded in 1984, and prior to July 1, 1987 was administered for three years by the Florida Association of Colleges and Universities (FACU).

Russell V. Ewald, former executive vice president of the McKnight Foundation, presented to FACU a unique and historic opportunity at the 1983 annual meeting on September 30. He outlined a three-phase program for the state, to be administered by the association. Further, he agreed to commit at least 15 million dollars to the ''private/public partnership'' designed to help educators in Florida address some of their major higher education concerns. As part of this commitment, Florida was presented with a $10 million challenge: Every two dollars that the foundation provided required one dollar of state money in order to develop an education fund in perpetuity.

Representatives from both the private and public education sectors were involved in discussing a broad range of possibilities and concerns. These included former Governor Graham and his staff; Florida legislative leadership; then Chancellor of the State University System, Barbara Newell and her staff, as well as officers and the general secretary of FACU. The consensus was that Florida would continue its movement toward educational improvement and reform.

Below is the description of the four programs in three phases that were presented by the McKnight Foundation to FACU on September 30, 1983:

Phase One:

The McKnight Black Doctoral Fellowship Program was designed to increase significantly the numbers of qualified Black faculty in the colleges and universities of Florida. This program provided initially up to $1,000,000 per year for a three-year period for twenty-five fellows to pursue Ph.D.'s in the State of Florida.

The McKnight Minority Junior Faculty Development Fellowship Program provides up to $300,000 per year for fellowships designed primarily for non-tenured assistant professors. (A priority is given to Black and female candidates.) This program awards twenty fellowships which were designed to encourage excellence in both teaching and research.

Centers of Excellence (the original five) were initially funded for a maximum of $500,000 per year ($100,000 per center) for a three-year period. The centers formulate plans to expand the applicant pool of minority students for postsecondary education.

Articulation and Cooperation Projects were designed to establish communication and cooperation between secondary education and higher education institutions in Florida. Up to $150,000 per year was provided initially.

Phase Two:

The Challenge Grant was created to develop an endowment fund to ensure, at a minimum, the life of the two fellowship programs described above. By December 31, 1986, the challenge was met when the Foundation's grant of $10,000,000 was matched by the state's appropriation of $5,000,000. It was in Phase Two, on July 1, 1987, that the Florida Endowment Fund became fully operational.

Phase Three:

The expansion of the Public/Private Partnership represents the last phase. The broad purposes of the newly established Fund required the review and evaluation of existing programs, identification of educational needs, and the initiation of new programs to alleviate educational problems. A crucial aspect of this phase is the identification of individuals, foundations, and corporations willing to provide further financial support.

Program Results
Doctoral Fellowship Program

In March, 1989 the BDF accepted its sixth class of fellows. Since the program began in 1984, it has awarded a total of 142 fellowships. By August, 1989, there will be one hundred seventeen Fellows matriculating at nine of the eleven Florida participating universities in Florida. The first three Fellows received their Ph.D. degrees in 1988 and are gainfully employed at institutions of higher learning; two have remained in Florida! The program projects the total number of graduates for 1988-89 academic year to reach double-digits when ten to twelve Fellows receive their degrees.

In 1988, this pioneer program was recognized by and cited for its innovation and success by many professional publications and organizations including. *The Chronicle of Higher Education*, the American Council of Education's *Educational Record*, and *Black Issues in Higher Education*--all praising the program and its leadership. In addition, I initiated a public relations effort which took me to many national meetings--including those of the American Association of Higher Education, State Higher Education Executive Officers, National Black Student Retention Conference and National Association of State Universities and Land Grant Colleges--to heighten public awareness.

An external evaluation commissioned by the McKnight Foundation in 1987 credited the success of the program to several interdependent factors. Specifically, the report cited strong leadership, sizeable financial support, effective use of leverage, clear vision and careful implementation.

One of the evaluators noted the following concrete reasons for the program's early success:

1. A formalized networking and support system so that fellows can encourage each other
2. Strong emphasis on excellence and return on investment: The sense of doing your best and giving something back to the community where you live and work was definite.
3. Direct access to decision makers--including the program's president--who have the knowledge and power to solve problems.
4. The active involvement of fellows in their collective planning and development. They feel a part of something substantial, and their recommendations for improving the program are taken seriously .

The purpose of the BDF program has not changed since its inception: to increase the number of African-Americans who are qualified to become faculty members in higher education with Ph.D. degrees in critical disciplines. To accomplish this goal, twenty-five individuals are selected annually from a national pool and awarded up to $5,000 for tuition and fees and a stipend of $11,000. This support is still provided for a period of three years. An additional year of study, if required, is funded at the same level of support by the participating institutions, thereby providing four years of guaranteed financial support. Some participating institutions have now committed to the fifth and sixth year. At this present funding level, the fellowship supports study in more than forty-five disciplines.

What have we done? We have given academically talented African-Americans who otherwise may not have had it, the opportunity to pursue doctoral degrees and get involved in the highest level of advanced graduate study. The financial support which the BDF provides has clearly increased access and opportunity for Blacks to pursue doctoral degrees and, most importantly, expanded the pool from which qualified individuals can be selected for higher education faculty and administrative positions. There are now BDF fellows pursuing degrees in areas of study where, traditionally, representation has been minimal or non-existent in either academic programs or in the workforce. For example, fifty-three percent of the fellowship awardees are matriculating in the sciences. The remaining forty-seven percent of the fellows are matriculating in the Arts, Letters, Social Sciences or Professional Programs like Business and Public Administration. In the last application period, there was a significant increase in those interested in pursuing the various business specialties.

While there is diversity in the fields they chose to study, characteristically, the Fellows remain quite similar. They are female for the most part and from a Southern state. Most have done some graduate work and usually possess a master's degree. Nearly ninety percent of the Fellows are enrolled at public institutions. Theoretically, their early success can be attributed to the fact that they are seriously motivated and have a clear set of aspirations and goals.

Whatever the catalyst may be, this program has an unusually high retention rate: over eighty-four percent. Moreover, during fall 1987, approximately eighty percent of the matriculating fellows maintained a grade point average of 3.0 and above. Twenty-three Fellows have successfully completed their course work and have been advanced to candidacy. Several others were expected to complete all course work during the 1989-90 academic year.

Only a very small number of students have left the program. Nine left because of unsatisfactory academic progress; seven left for personal reasons; one died in a drowning accident, and five left to pursue other professional fields which required advanced academic study in an area not supported by the BDF. Of the twenty-two who left, seven left with a master's degree.

We arrange an annual McKnight Fellows meeting, and it is one of the program highlights, according to most fellows. Here is where fellows share experiences and wisdom with other fellows while at the same time enjoy stimulation by local, state and national academic role models. It is the place where bonding occurs between and among fellows. At the request of a group of them, a mid-year meeting was started in 1987 because they felt that they needed the additional emotional boost provided by the gatherings.

I have taken the liberty of recording some of the comments from the fellows about the annual meeting because their feedback is an accurate index to the value of these sessions.

> *Participation in the annual McKnight Fellows meeting helps to lift up my spirits! This uplifting comes both from external and internal support. The administrative staff serves as my guide as well as my 'reassurance zone.' The family of Black doctoral Fellows and Junior Faculty Fellows lends that intimate touch to let you know someone cares. Also, they remind me that solidarity is ever present because "We're all in this together," and it is a great thing to be in it with others.*

> *I am inspired by this opportunity to be associated with Black and other minority scholars who are taking their developed skills seriously. I, too, want to produce results that will make a social, scholarly difference. I am motivated not only to graduate, but to graduate with skills that will enable me to perform scholarly research and teach in my discipline competently, creatively and insightfully. I am inspired.*

Even the external evaluator of the program talked about the common bond and the desire to be the very best in their selected fields of study: to excel and make a contribution to humankind, especially to Black people as well as to their discipline and the community and university where they live and work.

Here is what the evaluator wrote: "I was inspired and motivated by these young people who in many instances were first generation educated Black professionals like myself."

Junior Faculty Fellowship Program

The McKnight Minority Junior Faculty Development Fellowships (JFDF) are designed to encourage excellence in teaching and research by providing assistance to full-time minority (especially Black and female) junior faculty employed at institutions throughout the state. The fellowship provides a full academic year of funded leave for fellows to pursue graduate work, special academic interests and research activities which will favorably affect their teaching, eventual tenure or promotional status at their home institutions.

We hope to improve junior faculty retention rates and increase the number of them advancing through the professional ranks. S i n c e its beginning, a total of one hundred thirteen fellowships have been awarded. Seventy-nine were awarded to African-American faculty, nine to Hispanic faculty and twenty-five to white female faculty.

The retention rate for Junior Faculty Fellows has also been exceptional. Only two fellows have withdrawn from the program over a five-year period. Furthermore, three fellows have received their doctorates, and five have subsequently received promotions and/or tenure.

Characteristically, the Junior Faculty Fellows are female, Black and at or below the assistant professor rank. The past and present recipients are from twenty-six Florida higher educational institutions. Although the fields of academic specialty are varied, there is an attempt to give preference to those disciplines identified as critical and underrepresented.

More than half of the Junior Faculty Fellows have used the fellowship year to pursue research and publication interest; 42.4 percent pursued doctoral course work or completed dissertation research, and 3.3 percent pursued other professional and developmental activities.

During the 1987-88 operational year, some new criteria were added by the board of directors for this program. These yardsticks are not expected to change the basic thrust of the program but to expand the possibilities for independent institutions in particular since many of the independent colleges and universities in Florida have minimal to no minority representation on their faculties and staff. The expanded criteria offer an opportunity for some independent institutions and others to become more culturally diverse.

When I looked at the evaluations of the JFDF program, again it seemed to me from their reflections, some of which follow, that we are on the right track:

The McKnight program allowed me to devote an entire academic year to research. From a quantitative perspective, it allowed me to increase my number of publications and will, I believe, assure that I get tenure. More important to me are the aspects which cannot be measured quantitatively. As a scientist, I must confess that my knowledge of Black history has not been extensive. In fact, I have never been excited about history of any kind. That has changed because of my participation in this program. I am a person who has a strong "inner drive," and yet I must confess that I went away from the Fellows conference with a "warm" feeling inside. I would never have experienced these things had I not participated in the McKnight Junior Faculty Fellowship Program. I found it to be very inspirational, and I have made several friends from other institutions in the state whom I would never have met without this program. That is important to me.

Being awarded a McKnight Junior Faculty Development Fellowship has been a dream come true. I don't believe I would ever have finished my Ph.D. degree without the McKnight fellowship. The fellowship means that a priority which I have long held in abeyance finally gets to be realized. Being 'ABD' has meant falling short. That has not been a comfortable posture for me. The fellowship means moving on. I'm elated!

The McKnight program has been an excellent opportunity for me to meet and interact with other Black, female scholars. It has been a meaningful opportunity for me to see, feel and hear that I am not alone in my feelings or experiences. It has been a time of revitalization of my commitment and reassessment of my motivation. This has been an excellent source of rejuvenation of my determination to complete my doctorate. The conference helped me to put in perspective the significance of my moving forward in this way. I am eternally grateful for this opportunity.

There is a saying that God does not always answer our prayers when we want Him but He's right on time. That was truly my situation. The McKnight fellowship was an answer to my prayers and right on time. The McKnight program not only gave me the opportunity to finish my doctorate and receive my degree, but it also gave me the opportunity to engage in some unique research which would not have been possible otherwise. I'm very thankful.

Centers of Excellence

We established Centers of Excellence (COE) to help develop the missing characteristics in our African-American youth. The missing link is the tradition, the culture of group achievement; the sense that it is all right to be smart and to excel in school.

The primary purpose of the centers, therefore is to expedite the formation of this culture. In the process, we shall heighten the self-esteem of African-American youth, inspire and nurture their aspirations and prepare them for college entrance and successful matriculation. While pursuing these goals, the centers also address issues related to the enrollment and subsequent retention of Black students in the educational systems of Florida.

Since January 1985, the number of programs and participants has continued to increase and program quality has been enhanced. Now there are a total of ten centers, the first five being located in Madison, Gainesville, Orlando, Tampa and Miami. Five additional Centers of Excellence were funded in January 1986 as a result of a $150,000 allocation by the Florida legislature. They are located in Pensacola, Tallahassee, Jacksonville, St. Petersburg and Ft. Lauderdale. These newer COE's that were funded by the state and the McKnight Foundation began with $50,000 each.

Again in 1987, the legislature provided another $150,000 for the new centers and the McKnight Foundation added $130,000 to allow for the continuation of the new and old centers. During the 1988 session, the legislature increased its appropriation to $300,000 ($30,000 per Center) for the ten COE's.

Each center must accomplish four minimum requirements:

Involve Black churches in a significant portion of center activities;

Develop Academic Enrichment Centers in the given communities to supplement student learning experiences;

Induct high-achieving Black students into the McKnight Achievers Society, and

Sponsor county-wide and regional Black History and Culture Brain Bowl competitions leading the state competition which occurs in Tampa each winter.

Center of Excellence programs vary considerably, basically conforming to the personalities of their leadership and the local communities. The centers, however, continue to focus on individual and group motivation, academic skill development, cultural enrichment, career awareness and increased exposure to higher education institutions and programs.

As expected, community support and involvement in center activities have continued to increase. But Black church involvement as an integral part of the Center of Excellence is expanding more slowly than desired. There is no question that Black churches have the capacity to expand the COE concept rapidly across Florida. They provide space, leadership for the various activities, and are the source of much of the volunteer support.

Yet, community support that is broader based is much more evident. Local schools, school boards, businesses, higher education institutions, corporations, city governments, city officials, social clubs, professional groups and other organizations have cooperated with the centers to the extent that approximately 1400 persons statewide with professional and technical skills at all levels have participated as volunteers. This voluntary support is central to the success of the COE's, and without that kind of backing, it would be impossible to sustain this critical effort.

Articulation and Cooperation

The purpose of the articulation and cooperation component is to help develop creative forums, programs and processes. Following are highlights of the projects.

PROJECTS	MAJOR ACCOMPLISHMENTS
Florida Institute of Education	**Subject Area Articulation**--Has begun replicating an articulation model throughout the state; is preparing a procedures manual for conducting subject area articulation meetings and writing agreements.
Gulf Coast Community College	**Articulation Council**--Developed a "Homework Hotline" in Bay County; coordinated a tri-county community workshop which resulted in implementation of a summer academic enrichment program for math and English. Also developed the Bay County Enrichment Center modeled after our Centers of Excellence.
Hillsborough County Consortium	**Community Relations**--Is developing a calendar of major Black events in the Tampa Bay area; co-sponsored a College Readiness Club workshop on financial aid, admissions and testing.
Indian River Community College	**Postsecondary Motivation**--Facilitated Thirty (30) Saturday workshops at St.Lucie County College designed to motivate and prepare Black students for college--including academic assistance and personal problem solving; has begun afternoon and Saturday sessions in Indian River County.

Manatee	**Manatee Teacher Preparation**--Organized
Community	the Articulation Office; hired staff; hosted a
College	student services staff meeting; has begun
	facilitation of content workshops (math,
	English, social science).

To extend the reach of the COE's, Academic Enrichment Centers (AEC's) were established in the centers to provide supplemental learning experiences running parallel with the public schools.

McKnight Achievers Society

The most outstanding and consistent program activities at all centers are the McKnight Achievers Society and the Black History and Culture Brain Bowl.

The McKnight Achievers Society (MAS) rewards academic excellence and cultural accomplishments. Students inducted into this prestigious organization have made significant academic achievements or have been recognized for outstanding artistic or other cultural abilities. They are selected on the basis of academic excellence and therefore must have an A or B grade point average and no fewer than two A's. No C grades are acceptable unless they are in advanced or honors classes. Achievers recognized for artistic and cultural talents have competed in and won competitions in both local and broader communities.

A McKnight Achiever must...
> be enrolled in school at any level, kindergarten through college;
> be nominated by an adult (inclusive of parents) in the state;
> be sponsored by an adult in the state who will minimally purchase
>> the McKnight Achiever's jacket, and agree to serve as a
>> "significant other" in the Achiever's life;
> be an exemplary role model for other students to emulate;
> submit a written report on a completed community service project
>> each year.

Approximately 3000 young African-American Students--most in grades one through seven--have been inducted into the MAS over the past four years. The MAS gets to the heart of developing a group achievement tradition within the Black community by supporting the view that the greater the recognition of Black youth for the good that they achieve, the more the community can point to the many positive examples to be emulated.

So a critical facet of this program is the community service requirement. It is so important for Black youth to understand the value of giving back to the community and to see that by reaching back and pulling others along, the entire community prospers.

The Concept of Empowerment

A distinguishing characteristic of the Florida effort was the sense of empowerment that it gave to the African-American community. To be sure, this kind of effort was not new to the McKnight Foundation itself, which had similar kinds of projects in their native Minnesota and have continued that tradition with their current rural initiatives in Minnesota. But the Black community is simply not accustomed to having enough financial resources made available to fully concentrate on the tasks to be accomplished. It was not just the amount ($17 million), but also the structure of the financial arrangement ($10 million challenge grant for endowment) that was empowering. To endow the essence of a program in perpetuity provides a sense of security that frankly is unprecedented in the African-American community.

But this is precisely the kind of philanthropic leadership and foresight that needs to be replicated and seriously discussed in the foundation world. The notion that multi-year grants would somehow lead to a commitment by the recipient to continue the worthwhile funded effort after the external support had ended has been a miserable failure. How many times have institutions and agencies answered the last question on the application form--how do you plan to continue the activities after funding has ended--with an affirmative response? The question generally was, how does the recipient plan to carry on the activities stated in the proposal once funding has ended?

Glowing optimistic language is generally conjured up by the applicant to reflect commitment beyond the funding period. Resources were frequently manufactured to demonstrate the ability to continue the project. But how, the agencies should have asked, would institutions with a history of financial difficulty or of very modest financial means be able to support an initiative requiring great resources, given the uncertainty of what the future might bring? However, it did not seem to matter to the funding sources or was just overlooked in the effort to meet the agency's objectives.

This historic undertaking depended greatly upon the cooperation of the state legislature and the post-secondary educational institutions. And the private/public collaborative model is one that holds tremendous promise for the decade of the nineties and into the twenty-first century. If anything has been learned from the "New Frontier," "The Great Society" and beyond, it is that government has a role to play but cannot and should not in many instances act alone. The experience of the 1980's also tells us that "the safety net" is very porous for those who need it most. The private/public cooperative model may be the very strategy needed to mount a meaningful attack on many of society's ills in the future.

Lessons Learned

The Florida Endowment Fund (FEF) is still a new organization with only eight years of experience. However, in those years, there are certain lessons that were learned.

First, a number of factors contributed to our early success in producing Black Ph.D.'s. By centralizing the recruitment and application process, the FEF has been able to increase the applicant acceptance rate by relieving the various academic departments of the costs associated with recruitment and admission. Further, a system of internal and external support has contributed greatly to the early accomplishments of the program. Expansion of the pool of applicants, many of whom do not fit the traditional profile of a preferred doctoral student, has been one of our major achievements and relies upon the contention that the African-American experience in America and in higher education has not been typical itself. Given this reality, why would one expect that their academic profiles would be typical of those of the mainstream?

What really counts--and this needs to be emphasized--is performance, not traditional expectations on the front end. Therefore, the ability to provide a consistent, annual opportunity for bonding through the annual fellows meetings, along with general academic support and professional development support through our travel-supported research presentations is making a real difference in producing African-American academicians.

Finally, the quasi-public nature of the FEF eliminates much of the institutional infighting that goes on in the battle for resources and turf. Institutions are becoming more supportive of the program with each passing year. And in the final analysis, success breeds success and increases confidence in the ability of the McKnight Fellows to succeed.

10

Let Him Speak Who Has Seen With His Eyes

Where are we and where must we go in order to meet the challenges of this decade and the twenty-first century? Many of the answers and directions are with us and are not as complicated and complex as we educators and policy-makers say they are. Clearly, we cannot continue along the same path with the same compass. Disproportionality must be reduced significantly or eliminated by the next century. In other words, African-American children must succeed at a rate that equals or exceeds that of their majority counterparts. Anything less perpetuates the cruel myth that our children are innately inferior.

Where are we?

Since school failure and dropout continue to be disproportionately high among African-American children, we should ask a very fundamental question of ourselves: Are there any models or is there specific evidence leading us to believe that the educational system, as we know it, has serious promise for educating African-American and other socially disadvantaged children? And if we examine the demographic data and recognize that there are going to be more youngsters who fall into the category of the ''dark and the different,'' can we expect more of these children to fail? The answer is yes.

Given this prognosis, it seems to me that we must be more aware of what appears to be one of the most dangerous and troubling realities to come out of the 1980's--the growing gap between the haves and the have-nots, particularly as it relates to the distance between white and African-American communities. This gap says in no uncertain terms that the trends of the sixties and seventies have clearly been reversed in terms of group progress and that the policies of the eighties unmistakably intervened to retard and in some instances reverse that progress. Because of this changed national political climate, it is clear that there are some additional conservative and reactionary forces at work that do not give us concerned about black empowerment much reason for unbridled optimism.

Several conclusions can be drawn if we examine this climate, and three trends in particular present us with some specific challenges and hurdles that must be negotiated. What I find most interesting about them is that each has relevance to education as a process as well as an institution.

First, at a time when the demographics tell us that we can expect one third of this nation to consist of ethnic minorities by the year 2000, the conservative shift that has taken place over the last twenty-five years exhibits complete disregard for racial tolerance and cultural diversity. In fact, racial intolerance seems to be on the rise. We need look only at the visible Klan resurgence in many areas of the country; or the increased number of racial incidents on college campuses, or the turning back of the clock by the U.S. Supreme Court and other legislative actions at the state levels. I cannot help but have serious doubts about our ability to maintain the progress and gains made in the two previous decades, and whether there is the potential for future progress to be made.

I am also concerned that the recent influx of Asian-Americans to this country has fueled some additional discussion about supposed African-American inferiority. While touting very highly the progress of these new citizens from the Pacific Rim, many will say, including former President Reagan, that the progress being made by these ''new arrivals'' reinforces the myth that the indigenous population of African Americans does not have the wherewithal or the will to succeed in the mainstream. Therefore, the accomplishments of some visible Vietnamese, Koreans, Laotians, Cambodians and Filipinos serve to reinforce the negative stereotypes and beliefs in our society about African-American inferiority.

Continued racist immigration policies will continue to support such contentions. The example of small boat loads of Haitians being turned around in Florida waters while hundreds of Cubans are allowed into Miami each day as a result of U.S. Government policy is a case in point.

The second trend which I believe to be of considerable significance is the movement of our society from a post-industrial base to one centered on information and technology. This shift is creating an even larger gap between those who traditionally have been left out of the mainstream and their majority counterparts. There is no question that this change will require more of our citizens to be equipped with the abilities to compete and survive in an information-based society.

If we look at the job stratification of a few decades ago, we would find that six percent of the workforce was in professional, technical and managerial jobs. At that time, we were basically an agrarian and manufacturing society that did not require a highly educated workforce to the extent that it does today. Now, rather than six percent, more than thirty-three percent of the workforce can be classified as professional, technical and managerial. One can readily see from this data that there has been a major shift in the workforce and African Americans must be able to hold their own within the new parameters defined by this shift.

This second trend carries with it strong implications for the ''dark and the different.'' Too often our communities will lack the financial resources necessary to foster the interaction of African-Americans with the latest technology. Without sufficient resources to purchase the technology and make it an integral part of the educational process, our community will see the gap widen. So the failure to provide these children with the modern technology and the related skills required to be manipulators of information will relegate them to a subordinate position in the established social order.

The natural consequence of this deficit will leave us with a large proportion of African-American children lacking motivation and inspiration, condemned to being even more dispossessed in the land of their birth than they are now. It therefore becomes critically important that whatever educational strategies we possess for reform must take into account these very complex overlays associated with the technological transition our society is experiencing.

At the same time, we must be keenly aware of the society's low expectation level for these children: they will not be expected to have the ability to utilize the new technology effectively, even if it were available.

A third trend is the newly emerging belief on the part of America's business and industrial leadership that the country cannot remain internationally competitive because of what the leadership sees as a workforce problem attributable to the failures of the education system. In the minds of many, the failures are linked to the increased presence of more socially disadvantaged minorities in the system. Therefore, they see a need to take some revolutionary action to advance educational reform.

As we look at the demographic trends, the schools as we know them will have a greater number of students who will represent the ''dark and the different.'' The disproportionate failure of African-Americans and other minority groups in the past twenty years gives us little hope that this issue is any better understood. There has simply been no evidence over the last twenty years that gives us any tremendous hope and anticipation that these issues are any better understood now than they were for the last three or four decades.

I have serious reservations about whether the schools, as well as the educational process, can educate and train sufficient numbers from minority groups to meet not only workforce needs, but also to allow them to play a more viable role as participants in the American future.

There is no doubt that the business community is taking the issue of the future workforce seriously. The question of literacy and preparation is central. Rightly or wrongly, the community is focusing specific attention on the schools as the institution responsible for training the needed workforce. Business leaders are using their significant influence and resource base to forge educational reform. To me, this enthusiasm remains rather consistent with what I have been saying, because we must be ever mindful that historically, no significant change takes place within education that is generated from within the institution. Unfortunately, when major change occurs, it usually finds its stimulus from outside the framework of the institution or system.

One of the dangers and cautions upon which we must focus is that these latest changes, such as school-based management and magnate schools, *may very well get implemented but not really touch on the problem of disproportionality.* All of the changes mentioned above could be successfully implemented--with teachers and principals having more on-site decision-making and authority over budget and curriculum--and we would still find that African-American and other socially disadvantaged children are failing at a disproportionate rate when compared to their majority counterparts.

Therefore, whatever the reform thrust, it becomes paramount that the issue of disproportionality be kept very much in the forefront of whatever plans and strategies are formulated on local, state and national levels.

Future Considerations

The twenty-first century is less than a mere ten years away. I believe that the nineties is clearly a make or break decade. Business cannot continue as usual if America is to maintain the world leadership position that it has enjoyed since World War II. If this country is to achieve the incredible heights that are within its grasp both as a nation and as a member of the world community, Americans of all races must do better with the development of human resources. This country will need more diverse education and workforce participation by those who are "dark and different." It will need to develop the skills of minorities more effectively and in many new areas. Whether they are African-American, Native-American, Mexican-American, Puerto Rican-American or the new Americans from the Pacific Rim countries, these individuals must be seen as part of the solution. Somehow our educational system must become as adept at encouraging and producing desirable achievement levels from these groups as it is with the more affluent majority population. It is only good business to do so, and absolute idiocy not to find ways to make it happen.

My vision and blueprint for making this happen has been laid out in the preceding chapters. I speak because I have seen with my eyes. The blueprint starts with the absolute belief that all children can learn barring significant mental deficiencies; the stories are legendary in America about poor beginnings and revolutionary achievement. It continues with the fact that the issue of nature versus nurture is one that we understand and recognize, and it is clarified by the realization that it is time to wipe clean historical inaccuracies about minorities so that accurate information can produce new ideas and new understandings. The need for a multiculturally based curriculum that recognizes the contributions of African-Americans and other minorities is absolutely essential in a pluralistic society. When children cannot relate to not only the subject matter, but also to the purveyors of that subject matter, the inability leaves a negative effect on their ability to learn. New strategies for improving achievement and performance have to be bolstered, nurtured and reinforced from outside the school setting. The schools, by their very nature, are not prepared or equipped to do what needs to be done to accomplish the objectives described.

Therefore, communities must initiate and develop strategies for motivating, mentoring, nurturing and loving all of its children. Short of some massive efforts on the part of caring adults and communities, the future will not hold the promise that is so familiar to all of us. To use Alexander Solzhenitsyn's *Gulag Archipelago,* "You dwell on the past you lose an eye, you forget the past you lose both eyes." It is critical that we not lose both eyes. The children are our future, and it is up to us to make the difference for the "dark and the different." Nobody said the road would be easy!